THE DRUG USERS

the Drug Users

The Psychopharmacology of Turning On

A. E. WILDER SMITH

D. Sc., Ph.D., Dr. es. Sc., F.R.I.C.
Professor at the University of Illinois
at the Medical Center, Chicago

HAROLD SHAW PUBLISHERS   WHEATON, ILLINOIS

FIRST EDITION

LIBRARY OF CONGRESS CATALOG CARD NUMBER: 73-86528

Contents

Prologue

Spiritual nature, like bodily nature, will be served; deny it food and it will gobble poison. —C. S. Lewis

There are a thousand people hacking away at the branches of evil for every one striking at the roots. —Henry David Thoreau

Introduction

DRUGS USED SINCE EARLY TIMES

It is a mistake to imagine that the use of drugs is uniquely characteristic of our technically and medically advanced civilization. Drugs have been used for the treatment of bodily ailments such as boils, carbuncles, leprosy and tuberculosis since very early times. There is evidence that the ancient Chinese used, as a standard treatment for carbuncles, moldy soybean flour in which there will surely have been present the organism *penicillium notatum,* the mold which produces penicillin today.[1] The use of foxglove for treating dropsy and cardiac failure was known to herbalists long before it was discovered in a herbalist's formula and used by Dr. William Withering, a physician and botanist, in the eighteenth century. So the application of drugs, particularly those of plant origin—but not excluding those of animal origin, such as toad skin—has been known and developed from earliest times for the treatment of bodily ills.

But early man not only knew quite a lot about drug therapy for bodily ailments, infections, etc.; he also used drugs in the treatment of mental illness. The Hindus are known to have used *Rauwolfia serpentina* roots for centuries for the treatment of insanity.[2] *Rauwolfia* is used today as a source of reserpine, well known as a tranquilizer and antihypertensive agent.

However, the use of drugs for treating somatic (bodily) and psychic (mental) illnesses did not exhaust the applications of drugs known to early man. The Chinese Emperor Shen Nung, who lived about 2700 B.C., described the use of cannabis (marijuana) prepared from the top of the flowering hemp plant.[3] The emperor knew that when this drug was smoked it produced a state of dreamy altered consciousness; disconnected, uncontrollable ideas; the recall to memory of things long since forgotten; and other signs of marijuana smoking so well publicized today. He also described the vivid hallucinations and exaltation produced by a high dose, the inner joyousness and the uncontrollable laughter, together with the reverie and depression which may follow the use of marijuana.

RELIGIOUS PRACTICES

From man's earliest history it has been known that religious practices such as meditation, singing and chanting, together with the carrying out of complicated solemn rituals, may induce changes of consciousness in man's mind. Coupled with these exercises it was discovered that fasting and isolation from fellowship with other human beings also bring on changed states of consciousness. Up to modern times, mystics have been a recognized element of most civilizations (except perhaps the modern technical one!) and these mystics have experienced changed states of consciousness as a result of intense concentration and application to the end in view. They considered that their asceticism paid off in the joy, peace, serenity and "difference from other men." That is, they knew how to "turn on" without the help of drugs, though the exercises they practiced cost them a lifetime of hardship.

Thus we may conclude that man from his earliest history has practiced changing his state of consciousness (or "turning on") and that he has gone about it the hard way by fasting, becoming a hermit or a monk, practicing penances and offering sacrifices by complicated rituals, as well as by means of suitable drugs. Today human nature has not changed much in that a good percentage of the race still desires a changed state of consciousness. But man no longer seeks it the hard way, the religious way, involving hardship, fasting, isolation and religious ritual, but by the easy way. That is, he would rather take a pill to enjoy "instant mysticism." He wishes to control everything "scientifically," even desiring to regulate the change of his state of consciousness. He wants to be able to "turn on" and also to "turn off" at will. However, it must not be forgotten that even ancient man knew how to do this with certain poisonous mushrooms.

Though the use of hallucinatory drugs for religious purposes was well known in early times, their use for such purposes is known today in certain so-called primitive tribes of man as well as in Dr. Timothy Leary's League for Spiritual Discovery!

Thus we are severely mistaken if we imagine that the recent outbreaks of drug abuse for psychic and religious purposes are a new phenomenon. There is nothing basically new in the use or abuse of a majority of these types of drugs. What are new, however, and must therefore be kept steadily in view in discussing this subject, are the epidemic proportions now being assumed by drug abuse in a large number of the most developed and industrialized Western nations. Greenwich Village, Haight-Asbury and Old Town represent an epidemic flare-up of the old phenomenon of drugs used for psychic purposes.

QUESTIONS ON DRUGS

The questions we now propose to ask are:

1. What are the properties of the LSD type of drug and other currently abused drugs?
2. Do we know the basic causes of this epidemic of LSD and other drug abuse in Western society?
3. Will drug abuse in general get worse or better?
4. What can be done to help those under the influence of drugs?
5. Is it true, as the proponents of some drugs maintain, that some of these drugs (e.g., LSD), are truly psychedelic drugs (drugs which *expand* the consciousness), enriching the life and consciousness of the initiate?

By giving short résumés on the pharmacological properties of some psychedelic, tranquilizing and other drugs, and an analysis of the possible reasons why society—particularly young Western society—uses drugs, we will endeavor to indicate possible ways to get out of the present drug epidemic. We will also come to some conclusions on the basic lessons that our Western civilization may draw from the present predicament of our affluent society.

FACTORS CAUSING DRUG EFFECT

It should always be remembered that any effect a drug may exercise upon a man, animal or plant is the result of these two clearly definable factors:

1. The properties intrinsic to the drug itself. For example, morphine is an addictive analgesic substance—those are its intrinsic properties.
2. The attributes, character and properties of the animal, plant or human ingesting the drug as well as the psychical and physical environment.

It is often assumed that a drug in itself produces certain well-defined effects. But it is forgotten that the drug combines with the organism it affects to produce something new. Changing the drug may produce as noticeable an effect as changing the organism with which it combines. Just as chlorine combines with hydrogen to produce hydrogen chloride—which shows entirely different properties from those of the chlorine and hydrogen separately—and hydrogen and oxygen combine to form water—which again has new properties—so it is with drugs. The same drug may show different effects on different people. It "combines" with different people to produce different "compounds," which may be as different as water is from the hydrogen and oxygen from which it was produced. This example may be exaggerated, but the principle is correct.

This is what is meant by the terms "set" and "setting." In general "set" is one's attitude to the drug experience, and "setting" indicates the conditions and environment under which the drug experience takes place. The drug itself, the set and the setting are all important factors in determining the nature of the drug experience, although neither set nor setting will prevent an undesirable effect from being experienced under some circumstances. This is merely another way of saying that any drug experience is compounded of three main factors: (1) the nature of the drug itself, (2) the nature of the individual taking the drug, and (3) his circumstances at the time.

Western civilization is today encountering drugs of vastly increased potency and range of action on the one hand, together with the greatly changed environmental circumstances under which men live, on the other hand. We will examine both the drug factor and the environmental factor, for the drug epidemic can be understood properly only if one takes both factors thoroughly into consideration. In Part I the drug factor is considered. In Part II the environment, including that part of it which is man's nature, is treated.

[1] Louis Weinstein, "Chemotherapy of Microbial Diseases" in Louis S. Goodman and Alfred Gilman (eds.), *The Pharmacological Basis of Therapeutics,* p. 171.
[2] Murray E. Jarvik, "Drugs Used in the Treatment of Psychiatric Disorders" in *ibid.,* p. 178.
[3] Jerome H. Jaffe, "Drug Addiction and Drug Abuse" in *ibid.,* p. 299.

Part One
The Drug Factor

1. Lysergic Acid Diethylamide-25 (LSD): Its Pharmacology

SOME PROPERTIES OF LYSERGIC ACID DIETHYLAMIDE-25 (LSD)

lysergic acid diethylamide-25

Before one can analyze the significance of the drug situation in our society it is first necessary to know something of the pharmacological nature of the drugs concerned. Thus it will be necessary to look into the exact effect that psychedelic (consciousness-expanding) and related drugs exercise on the human body and mind. That is, we must first examine the pharmacology of LSD. Then, when we are familiar with the drug's properties, we will be better able to link them with our society's problems.

The drug is fairly easy to synthesize from lysergic acid by formation of the diethylamide by standard technique.

Natural Sources

Two main natural sources of lysergic acid and its amide are known: (1) ergot and (2) some varieties of morning-glory plants. The d-lysergic acid amide is an hallucinogen of one-tenth of the power of LSD. Ololiuqui (*Rivea corymbosa* or *Ipomoea sidaefolia* or *Turbina corymbosa*), a large woody vine, contains both ergine and lysergic acid amide in the leaf and stem.[1]

A good account of the occurrence of lysergic acid amides in nature has been given by K. R. Kapper.[2] LSD is believed to be one of the most active drugs—on a weight-for-weight basis—of any type known, though there are many drugs with similar properties which are less potent. Botulism is also caused by exceedingly small amounts of an active agent. It is believed that there may be one more hallucinatory drug, at present classified for military reasons, which is about four times more active (weight for weight) than LSD itself. The possible use of such drugs for military purposes is obvious. If a fog, containing the drug suspended in droplets, were distributed over enemy lines, those inhaling it would soon (within twenty to sixty minutes, according to the dose) suffer severe psychic disturbances and hallucinations. They might imagine their enemies were angels, spirits, pigs or tomatoes; that their gun barrels were crooked or sugar canes, and that their commanding officer was the cook or the enemy commander! So the military significance of a really powerful hallucinogen might be great, especially if it were cheap, chemically stable and easily handled.

Factors Determining Drug Effects

To understand any drug action it is basic to remember that

the effect a drug produces depends on the drug itself as well as on the subject taking the drug. Thus both the drug and the person taking it determine the end effect of the drug. This is particularly true in the case of psychopharmacology where some subjects are sedated by a certain dose of barbiturate or morphine, whereas others even may be stimulated (for a time) by the same relative dose. Varying temperaments react in varying ways to a constant dose of LSD. Some may even show little effect. Canines, felines and man all react differently to barbiturates. Lions are said to react to barbiturates with a bellyache! A human being in severe pain may react to barbiturates with agitation and hallucinations, whereas when he is not in pain the same person may react to the same dose of barbiturate with sleep.

This variation of drug response in varying subjects is well demonstrated in addicting drugs, where some individuals may get easily "hooked" and some may not. Reactions to LSD "trips" differ markedly. To repeat, one must keep steadily in mind that any pharmacological drug effect is due to three factors: (1) the drug employed, (2) the character (physical and psychic) of the individual exposed to the drug and (3) the conditions surrounding the individual and his current mood or psychological state. This explains why one drug may produce two different effects in two different individuals. A dose of LSD in a psychologically unstable person may precipitate a psychosis, whereas the same LSD dose may cause an ecstatic mystical experience in another individual. Further, the same dose of LSD may produce in the same person entirely different effects at different times, depending on whether he is elated or depressed when he takes the drug.

Dose Which Produces Hallucination

The dose of LSD required to produce "hallucination" in a normal person weighing 160 pounds lies between twenty-five and two hundred and fifty μgms (a μgm equals one microgram or one millionth of one gram) in one dose given orally or by injection. One hundred μgms will usually produce a "trip" lasting ten to twelve hours. The waiting period before the drug takes effect after application is between thirty to sixty minutes, according to the dose used. The higher the dose the shorter the waiting time.

Efforts have been made to smoke LSD by introducing it onto tobacco, but the results have not been so satisfactory from a hallucinatory point of view as when the drug is injected or taken orally.[3]

Strictly speaking, LSD and allied drugs do not produce hallucinations but rather distortions or accentuations of reality—unless the visual patterns as such can be classified as true hallucinations. In the later stages of delirium tremens, violent restlessness coupled with hallucinations produced by chronic alcohol intoxication, the patient may imagine that he is being attacked by gnomes, hobgoblins and little devils who stick their spears and daggers into his flesh, causing excruciating pain. He may cry out in terror at these imaginary attacks, although they are pure hallucinations, having no basis in reality. The little devils do not exist, nor do they really stick their spears into the patient.

In LSD intoxication the patient may gaze for hours in abandoned fascination at a light bulb or a cloth pattern. The most trivial objects may serve as bases for the same exaltation. But what the patient is seeing is actuality—a pattern or a light—even though it is distorted or accentuated. The pattern is real, the light is real, but both represent accentuated reality. The term "pseudohallucination" has been suggested for this type of distortion or accentuation of reality. The hobgoblins of delirium tremens have no basis in reality and are therefore true hallucinations. LSD and allied drugs (mescaline, marijuana, etc.) produce, in contrast, distortions or accentuations of real things, people, patterns, lights, etc., in other words, pseudohallucination. It is intended here, however, to use the term "hallucination" in its general meaning to cover also the idea of pseudohallucination.

DISCOVERY OF LYSERGIC ACID DIETHYLAMIDE-25 (LSD)

LSD is a relatively new synthetic drug and therefore was not known or used in ancient times. It shows some of the pharmacological properties of the older psychedelic drugs (mescaline, etc.) but is much more active, on a weight-for-weight basis, than anything previously known. Its hallucinatory properties were discovered by accident by Dr. Albert Hofmann in Basel, Switzerland, in 1943.[4] On April 16 of that year Dr. Hofmann was experimenting with ergot and oxytocic drugs (drugs which hasten childbirth, and increase the rapidity of labor; oxytocin also causes the release of milk in lactating mammals) and was working on the properties which stimulate the central nervous system in animals. He was synthesizing LSD itself for testing in this way and for use as an intermediate, when he was suddenly seized, while working at his laboratory bench, with vertigo (giddiness) and restlessness. Colleagues around him seemed to assume grotesque forms and shapes, so that Dr. Hofmann became alarmed and left the laboratory in a dreamlike state. He cycled home, clutching at his chest, and on arrival fell in a stupor full of colorful hallucinatory dreams. He noticed that there were few, if any, auditory effects.

When Dr. Hofmann recovered he had the insight to suspect the LSD with which he had been working as the cause of his experience. He became convinced that he had absorbed some substance through the skin, or in the form of a fine dust through the nasal septum, during experimentation.

A little later Dr. Hofmann resolved to try out his hypothesis that the LSD caused his experience. With the cooperation of his colleagues he ingested 0.25 milligrams (250 μgms) of the drug, which he thought would be an absolutely minute dose by ordinary drug standards. The effects were spectacular and his whole previous experience was repeated in the laboratory. Thus the powerful pharmacological effects of LSD were discovered by accident by the scientist who synthesized it for other purposes—a true case of serendipity.

THE PHARMACOLOGY OF LSD

Hofmann and his pharmacological colleagues Stoll and Rothlin at Sandoz S.A. in Basel, recognized immediately that their LSD produced symptoms resembling those shown by mescaline and cannabis (marijuana). They gave the substance to a colleague doing research in a psychiatric clinic, who confirmed that others experienced the same type of syndrome as Hofmann's. This fact was indeed fortunate, for one of Hofmann's closest colleagues (Stoll) had reported that he himself experienced nothing on taking LSD. The new drug might easily have been discarded and Hofmann's hallucinatory experience disregarded had not this further work in the psychiatric clinic been done immediately.

Pharmacologically and physiologically LSD acts as a sympathomimetic agent such as epinephrine and related biogenic amines.

Serotonin Antagonism

LSD is a powerful antagonist of 5-hydroxytryptamine (serotonin, 5-HT) but can also mimic its action.[5] It inhibits 5-HT-induced contractions of the rat uterus at a concentration of one microgram/ml. (10^{-9} gram) during ninety minutes.[6] But Welch[7] reports that LSD at 10^{-18} potentiates the concentration of the clam heart reacting to 10^{-9} gram of serotonin. This shows that LSD is a partial antagonist to 5-HT action before the blocking action becomes operative.

Dose Level

The most striking property of LSD is the low dose at which it acts. Of the 2 to 2.5 micrograms per kilogram of body weight taken by adepts, only about 1 percent is found in the brain, thus demonstrating the high sensitivity of certain brain receptors for it.

Excretion Route and Distribution

The probable preferred excretion route for orally ingested LSD is via the bile. One of the metabolites of LSD is

2-oxy-LSD, which is biologically inactive. Also the β-glucuronides of 2-oxy-LSD and 2-oxy-iso-LSD are formed and excreted.

LSD passes the blood-brain barrier easily. Its biological halflife is about 100 minutes in the monkey, 130 minutes in the cat and 7 minutes in the mouse. In man the halflife has been calculated as 175 minutes.[8]

After intravenous administration LSD has been found to concentrate in the pituitary, pineal and hippocampus, and to a small extent in the thalamus and hypothalamus. It does not concentrate in the visual cortex but rather in the deep visual reflex centers. Mescaline has been shown to follow a similar distribution pattern.

Tolerance

Tolerance to LSD develops rapidly so that increased dosages are needed to produce a constant response on successive days. LSD shows cross-tolerance to psilocybin and mescaline.

Mechanism of Action of LSD

The known partial antagonism between LSD and serotonin has provided the basis of the first suggested mechanism of LSD action. Small concentrations of LSD imitate 5-HT action, whereas higher concentrations antagonize it. However, since the exact neurophysiological role of 5-HT has not yet been elucidated, it will, of course, not be possible to say exactly how LSD produces its effect by imitating or antagonizing serotonin. That depends on elucidating the meaning of serotonin. In the rat LSD causes a 20 percent rise in 5-HT concentration, whereas reserpine causes a fall in 5-HT concentration. This effect may be linked with the potentiation of LSD effect in man produced by a dose of reserpine. The 5-HT rise in concentration in the rat takes place within fifteen to thirty minutes of dosing, which is also the time required for the animal to develop LSD signs. Signs disappear after about forty minutes.

Toxicity

LSD is of low toxicity. In the rabbit, which is highly sensitive to LSD, death is caused, as in other species, by respiratory failure. No LSD deaths have occurred in man as a result of direct toxicity. The greatest danger from LSD toxicity occurs when the drug is ingested by psychologically unstable persons, that is, by borderline psychotic and depressed individuals. Recurrent reactions have been noted in patients up to one year after the last use of the drug. Anxiety states with visual phenomena and depersonalization predominate.

Spiders have been fed on flies injected with LSD. The result has been that the spiders' web pattern has been modified.[9] Snails are very sensitive to LSD and react to small doses (0.01 micrograms/cc.) with a typical disorganized movement of the gastropod.[10] A male Asiatic elephant given 100 micrograms per kilogram of body weight (total dose 297 mgs) died.[11]

Since the drug has been in use for such a comparatively short time, not much can be said about its possible long-term toxic effects. However, reports show that LSD may cause biological as well as psychic damage (precipitating psychoses). *Pharmacy Science*[12] reported on the work of Dr. Cohen, Dr. Marinello and Dr. Back on human leucocytes, which were found to be damaged in their chromosomal structure by LSD. There was a marked increase in chromosomal abnormalities (breakage) after twenty-four to forty-eight hours of exposure to LSD. It is not yet known whether LSD chromosomal damage can be transmitted from one generation to another, but there is mounting evidence in this direction.[13]

Very recently it has been shown that LSD not only causes chromosomal breakage in adult users but also may do the same in unborn infants whose mothers have taken large doses of the drug.[14] Dr. Maimon Cohen of Buffalo's Children's Hospital and Dr. Kurt Hirschkorn of Mount Sinai Hospital, New York, tested eighteen adult users and four children exposed before birth to LSD. Two of the children whose mothers had exposed them to high doses of LSD showed breaks in about 13 percent of their chromosomes. The other two children had been exposed to low doses only and showed no changes.

The chromosomal breaks may lead to genetic defects, leukemia and autoimmune disorders, in which the body may destroy its own tissue. Previously it had been reported that no chromosomal damage had been discernable in the white cells of eight San Francisco "hippies."

This list of the known toxic properties of LSD may serve to summarize the material on hand to date:

1. It distorts consciousness, accentuating perception. Psychedelic action (consciousness *expansion*) is controversial.
2. It may produce tendencies to homicide and suicide.
3. It produces its effects long after ingestion has ceased (recall phenomenon).
4. It is probably toxic to human leucocyte chromosomes (causes breakage).
5. It distorts judgment and does not increase critical ability.
6. It is only slightly, if at all, habituating.
7. It would appear to be especially toxic for certain tissues in the brain and nervous system.

LSD intoxication or a "bad trip" may be antidoted by giving a tranquilizer such as thorazine, or by nicotinic acid.[15]

LSD–Psychopharmacology (Mechanism and Effects)

In LSD intoxication, reality is experienced in a variously emphasized form, but it is not known exactly how the drug works. The minutest quantities produce massive effects in the brain. It appears that LSD slows the rate of synaptic transmission of nerve impulses coming in as input to the brain decoding and processing centers. This means that the five senses (sight, hearing, feeling, taste and smell) each send in their messages through nerves across nerve junctions (synapses) to the brain centers, where incoming messages (impulses) are interpreted and decoded. The impulse input feed rate to the brain center would appear to be slowed down to a less than normal rate under the influence of LSD, which fact "perplexes" the brain and allows "focusing" on the incoming signals, which is not normally possible.

When the brain is thus allowed to focus on itself and its incoming impulses, a sort of introversion or frightened awareness of itself is produced. This is particularly true for messages concerned with vision and color. The LSD subject will concentrate and focus on the most commonplace objects, apparently in an ecstatic stupor.

The frightened awareness mentioned above may develop, in certain subjects, into overt panic. Even when LSD may be taken perfectly freely and willingly, the subject may find out afterward that the drug seems to be taking charge of him against his will. He feels he is being controlled and that he cannot rid himself of the psychological effects which have now hemmed him in. At this stage some subjects panic. They are exceedingly shaken and want to be released immediately from their state. They are prepared to "run away." Others become paranoid and are suspicious of everyone around them. They may lash out at or otherwise attack anyone near them. Tragedies have occurred at this stage, especially in cases where the LSD subject was armed.

The effects described above become more accentuated the larger the dose ingested. Dr. Baker of Toronto reports that grand mal (epileptic) seizures have been seen in patients given 1,500 or 2,000 micrograms of pure LSD. This is probably the only direct toxic effect observed so far, and it takes place only as a result of gross overdosing or in very susceptible patients.

The Recall Syndrome ("Flashback")

To observe an LSD "trip," it is sometimes regarded as important that the observer has never taken an LSD trip himself, because one trip can rob him for long periods of the critical ability necessary to compare and evaluate another's reaction to the drug. Merely watching a trip may produce a flashback trip in an observer who has previously taken LSD, even though he has not ingested LSD at the time of observation. Indeed, exposing normal men or women to gyrating color patterns in psychedelic surroundings may by itself produce the effect of LSD. That is, some effects of a trip can later be produced without having taken LSD again. The experience of a trip after an interval during which no further LSD was ingested is known as the recall syndrome and is referred to later in connection with the hallucinatory syndrome experienced in space medicine when astronauts are subjected to sensory deprivation. It represents a method by which the brain learns how to go into a psychedelic experience without the aid of a drug,[16] and is exceedingly important in interpreting the significance of psychedelic experience.[17]

It is generally agreed that it is possible to have flashback recurrences of a trip up to three years after an LSD-initiated trip without any further ingestion of the drug. A fit of anger or a family upset, the sound of certain kinds of music or even exposure to intense light may produce the original trip's symptoms without further ingestion. Such experiences may occur during night driving when drivers are exposed to bright oncoming lights. When the flashback occurs, instead of one pair of headlights being seen, thousands may seem to be converging on the confused driver who has no way of knowing which is the real pair of lights.[18]

A bad trip with paranoid symptoms may also be repeated in flashbacks. If during a trip a person imagined someone was about to murder him, such imaginations may reoccur many times for more than two years. Some LSD abusers report flashbacks occurring a few times monthly, whereas others have reported up to a hundred flashbacks daily. Obviously this is important in a highly technical society such as the one we live in.

[1]Abram Hoffer and Humphry Osmond, *The Hallucinogens,* p. 85.

[2]K. R. Kapper, "Lysergic Acid Derivatives in Morning Glory Seeds," in C. W. M. Wilson (ed.), *Adolescent Drug Dependence,* p. 78.

[3]*Ibid.,* p. 445.

[4]Murray E. Jarvik, "Drugs Used in the Treatment of Psychiatric Disorders" in Louis S. Goodman and Alfred Gilman (eds.), *The Pharmacological Basis of Therapeutics,* p. 205.

[5]J. H. Gaddum and K. A. Hameed, "Drugs Which Antagonize 5-Hydroxy-tryptamine," *British Journal of Pharmacology,* 9 (1954), 240.

[6]J. Lanz, A. Cerletti and E. Rothlin, article in *Helvetica Physiologica Pharmacologia Acta,* 13 (1955), 207.

[7]J. H. Welch, "Marine Invertebrate Preparations Useful in the Bioassay of Acetylcholine and 5-Hydroxytryptamine," *Nature,* 173 (1954), 955.

[8]N. J. Gearman, "The Pharmacology of LSD," *LSD, Man and Society,* eds. R. C. DeBold and Russell C. Leaf, pp. 149-50.

[9]P. N. Witt, *The Effect of Substances on the Construction of Webs by Spiders as a Biological Test.*

[10]H. A. Abrahamson and M. E. Jarvick, "Lysergic Acid Diethyl Amide, (LSD-25): Effect on Snails," *Journal of Psychology,* 40 (1955a), 337.

[11]L. J. West and C. M. Pierce, "LSD, Its Effects on a Male Asiatic Elephant," *Science,* 138 (1962), 1100.

[12]*Pharmacy Science* (Apr. 17, 1967), p. 24.

[13]*Science News,* Vol. 92 (Dec. 9, 1967).

[14]*Science Journal,* Vol. 4 (Jan., 1968), No. 1, p. 9.

[15]Hoffer and Osmond, p. 98.

[16]Donald B. Louria, "The Abuse of LSD," p. 41, and N. J. Giarman, "The Pharmacology of LSD," p. 157, *LSD, Man and Society.*

[17]W. A. Frosch, E. J. Robbins and M. Stern, "Untoward Reactions to LSD Resulting in Hospitalization," *New England Journal of Medicine,* 273 (1965), 1235.

[18]Margaret O. Hyde, (ed.), *Mind Drugs,* pp. 74-75.

2. Clinical Experience with LSD

SUMMARY OF THE EFFECTS OF AN LSD "TRIP"

After taking the drug, either absorbed from an aqueous solution on sugar (the "old-fashioned" way) or absorbed from solution onto blotting paper, which is subsequently dried (the modern method), the subject may wait some twenty to fifty minutes, according to the dose taken, for the effect to set in. The drug is rarely injected.

The first effect, after the ingestion of a small piece of paper impregnated with LSD, takes the form of withdrawal and reverie. Then follow acute brain symptoms. The mood becomes distorted, and inappropriate thoughts and actions may follow. Changes in thought follow a free flow of bizarre ideas which may include the feeling of persecution. Trivial events assume unusual significance and importance. Some LSD ahderents claim inspiration under the influence of the drug. After this stage, memory of recent events begins to fail, and events of early childhood, which may have been forgotten for years, impose themselves, that is, the subconscious rises to the conscious level.

Later on the I.Q. level sinks and intelligence defects appear (see p. 39).[1] Accompanying this, defects in judgment manifest themselves. The subject may, for example, be unable to see that his own gloves are larger than his wife's, and may swear hers are larger.

Essentially the LSD experience consists of changes in perception involving sight, sound, touch, body image and time. Colors seem to intensify or change, shape and spatial relations become distorted, objects may seem to pulsate, and two-dimensional objects may appear to be three dimensional. Some see halo effects around lights which may look like rainbows. Ordinary white light looks much brighter, and numerous colors surround it. Inanimate objects seem to assume import. Conversations may be heard but not comprehended. The sense of taste changes and food may feel gritty to the tongue.

Synesthesia

A further experience provoked by LSD is known as "synesthesia," which concerns the translating of one type of sensory experience into another. Thus, in listening to music the LSD subject will experience the vibrations of the music in his body, so the experience of music is translated into a tactile experience. In other cases the colors being viewed will be seen to beat in rhythm with the music. Again this illustrates the translation of one sensory experience into another.

The transfer of sensory stimuli in synesthesia can be very striking. The ringing of a phone can produce the illusion of visible waves of light emanating from it. Or flashes of sound waves may appear to radiate from a glass when it is struck.[1a]

Emotional Instability

Rapid changes of emotion are also characteristic of the LSD experience, and emotional instability may become marked. Giggling and laughing may characterize early LSD effects, but the laughter easily changes into sadness and crying with trivial changes of environment. A "tripper" may be ecstatically enjoying the blueness of the sky and the greenness of the grass because of the depth of colors he has never experienced before. But when the sun momentarily passes behind a cloud, he will suddenly find that the whole world is becoming gray and therefore unspeakably sad. One can sum up these experiences by saying that emotional instability and accentuation of mood characterize the LSD experience. This accentuation extends to quite trivial matters. For example, one may look at a stack of cups and feel amazed at how perfectly one cup fits inside another and how meaningful the stack of cups has become. Focusing of this type under the influence of LSD is sometimes referred to as a "hang up."

Reality accentuated. Talking to one student of mine (of first-class intelligence) about an LSD trip he had taken, it became clear that his main experience consisted in an accentuation of all reality. He was indignant on being informed that LSD might be an hallucinogen. He described with obvious delight the experience he had had of eating a pizza while on a trip. He had become so absorbed in playing with the cheese of the pizza on his plate—pulling it out into long threads, pushing it around in his mouth with his tongue, following the passage of one portion down his oesophagus into his stomach—that for pure ecstasy in physically manipulating his pizza he forgot the business of eating. He also experienced the "slowing down of time," which he attributed to focusing on the accentuated experiences of the trip. In summary, he maintained that LSD did not distort reality but accentuated all experience. Even the most trivial matters became sources of ecstasy. Light and shade in the most ordinary things so stood out as to make them each "a thing of beauty and a joy," but not "forever"!

Homicide and suicide. Tendencies to homicide and suicide are frequent. A subject may become convinced he can fly like a bird and may try to take off and fly out of a twentieth-story window. This is due to the fact that LSD subjects lose their sense of proprioception, in other words, awareness of their bodies and the position of their limbs, with a resultant floating feeling. Arms or legs may be held in one position for extended periods of time.

Recently the London newspapers reported the case of Leslie Wilson, a twenty-year-old laborer of Walthamstow. Wilson, who had obtained a supply of LSD at a club in Soho, London, was in the company of a young woman called Linda, whom the police were unable to trace. It was probably the first time Wilson had taken the drug, so he evidently did not fully understand its usual effects on the body. The girl, on the other hand, understood the effects of LSD quite well. Wilson was apparently dared to take the drug and, while under its influence, climbed to the top of a church roof, stripped off his clothing and jumped, possibly under the impression that he could fly under the influence of the drug. He died from his injuries.

Various forms of psychoses. Psychoses precipitated by LSD can take many forms. Sometimes the trip does not terminate normally and may go on for hours over the normal span. Some individuals continue in the paranoid state, being suspicious of being watched, criticized or persecuted, for long periods. One teenage boy locked himself in his room for several months, imagining that he was an orange and if anybody touched him he would turn into orange juice. Friends enabled him to live by bringing food to him every day. Others suffer from a guilt complex and feel so unworthy to live that they are sure they must die. Some lose contact with themselves and do not know who they are nor where they are going. Others panic and have to be forcibly restrained and put into the hospital before they do damage to themselves or others. One young girl had a bad LSD trip which lasted for four months, and even large doses of tranquilizers did not help her. Finally drastic electroshock therapy released her from the trip.[2]

Time Reversal and Other Sensory Changes

Time itself may seem to race, stop, slow down and even go backward. The phenomenon of time reversal can be remarkable. "In one case time was reversed and the subject who had picked up a cup of tea and drank from it was astonished to find he was sipping from the cup before he picked it up and before the tea was poured, as if a film has been run backward."[3]

Cloth seems to change its texture, becoming coarse and dry or fine and velvety. There are sensations of light-headedness, emptiness, vibrations and fogginess. Speech may be garbled and there may be difficulty in articulating certain words or syllables. Quiet sleep may be impossible for a time after a trip. Gradually, about ten hours after ingestion of a normal dose, the effects wear off, though the subject may remain bizarre for varying periods of time. Tolerance to the behavioral effects of LSD may develop with days of continued use, but physical dependence does not occur. Psychic dependence may develop, but it is seldom intense. Thus, most LSD devotees will use the drug when available but do not seem to experience serious craving for it when it is not available. In this way LSD resembles the marijuana type of drug, which is also nonaddicting.

After a number of hours the effects of LSD begin to wear off. Periods of LSD experience begin to alternate with periods of nonexperience when nothing happens at all. The active periods get shorter and less intense as time goes on. The effect of LSD thus diminishes. Fatigue, tension and recurrent pseudohallucination may persist for days or weeks after the drug ingestion, and psychological changes can last almost indefinitely.

GENERAL REACTIONS TO LSD

Not Serious Among Most Normal People

The incidence of serious reactions to LSD among normal

people given the drug is very low indeed. Donald B. Louria reports 0.08 percent as a representative figure.[4] Any drug used in normal therapy and showing such a low-toxicity incidence would be considered very harmless. But LSD reaction rates are definitely higher when the drug is used in conjunction with psychotherapy. Of such patients 0.2 to 2.0 percent showed prolonged psychiatric disorders. One out of 830 of such patients attempted suicide and one out of 2,500 was successful.[5] It is not possible to make any estimation of LSD reactions in cases where the drug was used without any supervision, but it is generally thought that incidence here may exceed 2 percent.

LSD-induced psychosis is today a recognized syndrome which often leads to hospitalization and may have severe consequences. The danger in LSD lies in its being ingested by unsuitable, unstable persons. In properly selected cases under controlled conditions, untoward reactions are rare. On the other hand, subjects harboring latent neurosis or psychosis show a high rate of toxicity incidents.

Adverse Reactions

The following adverse reactions have been noted:
1. schizophrenic reaction
2. prolonged state of LSD fright, especially in children who ingested the drug by chance
3. paranoid reactions
4. psychotic depression
5. anti- or dys-social behavior
6. convulsions
7. homosexuality
8. suicidal tendencies

LSD can induce violent behavior. Of those cases hospitalized some 12 percent showed uncontrolled aggressive tendencies and 9 percent attempted either homicide or suicide. One patient had attempted to murder his mistress' baby and another jumped in front of a train. Of patients hospitalized, about 75 percent had taken LSD on one to three occasions.

In other cases psychosis had developed only after forty or more ingestions of LSD.[6] At least one-third of the patients suffering from LSD psychosis had a history of psychopathology. The proportion may even be higher than this. It may be concluded, therefore, that LSD characteristically precipitates underlying neuroses or psychoses.

Most patients recovered from their LSD psychosis within about forty-eight hours after ingestion, but 16 percent were referred for long-term hospitalization. About half of these chronic LSD-psychosis patients had shown no previous psychopathology, showing that LSD is capable of inducing chronic and acute psychosis in previously apparently normal persons. It is not yet known if one or several LSD experiences are required to result in permanent mental derangement. All types of patients have shown induced psychoses—intellectuals, artists, ranchers, physicians, housewives, etc.

It has been noticed that those who use LSD chronically tend to withdraw from society and sever family ties. Such cases are known among fellow adepts as "acid heads" and spend their time in orgies of drug-induced introspection. They have ceased to be constructive members of society.

SOME MYTHS AND FACTS ABOUT LSD EFFECTS

Said to Promote Love

Certain proponents of LSD have circulated rumors to the effect that any woman who takes LSD in the presence of a man is forever in love with that man. Dr. Louria's answer to this myth is that no such alleged LSD postexperience corresponds to the actual facts.[7] The same myth has been circulated in Sweden about certain amphetamines. Marijuana habitués have reported the same thing about pot. There have, of course, been cases reported of a man and a woman taking LSD together and falling in love. But the same could be said of young men and women who go drinking together, go to church together or take a skiing trip in one another's company. It may be that in some cases LSD will accentuate the experience of falling in love, just as other experiences can be accentuated.

Powerful Aphrodisiac

Many statements have been made to the effect that LSD is a powerful aphrodisiac (agent for arousing sexual desire). The same property is reported of marijuana—supposedly a well-kept secret of marijuana habitués. But many couples have been in one another's presence under the influence of LSD and have shown no sexual interest whatsoever. Some believe that a majority would be incapable of sexual union when under LSD intoxication. However, in view of the phenomenon of synesthesia and accentuation of tactile experience, a few cases have reported an ecstasy of union. But these cases represent a minority, just as cases reporting a mystical experience—as opposed to a psychotic one—are also in a minority.

Imagination Catalyst

It is probably true that for certain creative individuals, such as composers, artists and painters, psychedelic drugs (including psilocybin) can act as "imagination catalysts." One composer of international reputation is reported to have taken psilocybin and under its influence to have "listened" to hallucinatory music, which he wrote down after the episode had worn off. It is unlikely that the drug would produce musical inspiration in a unprepared mind. It could produce nothing new, merely catalyzing that which was already present.

VARIOUS TYPES OF PSYCHEDELIC EXPERIENCE

Five main types of psychedelic[8] experience are distinguished.[9]

The Psychotic Experience

This can be described as a hellish experience where the

patient loses confidence in everyone and feels that he is going insane. This may be a desperate experience, the patient becoming panic-stricken and feeling hopeless. It is one of the more common LSD experiences, particularly in subjects of an unstable psychology.

An LSD patient in a drug-precipitated psychosis reported: "Time itself seemed to have frozen. . . . I had lost trust in the doctor . . . I was going insane. . . . I was two people in the same body . . . I had three minds, two that were insane and one perfectly normal. . . . The doctor looked like a devil to me . . . this would go on forever." [10] Panic and hopelessness characterize the psychotic state precipitated by LSD.

The Psychodynamic or Psycholytic Experience

Here the unconscious is thrust up into the conscious, and forgotten childhood and other experiences become fresh again.

In this state the unconscious or preconscious becomes conscious. Abreaction and catharsis, in which the patient recalls and relives a repressed traumatic emotional experience, characterize the condition. A skilled therapist is required to handle and guide the patient into the right channels.[11]

The Cognitive Experience

Lucidity of thought otherwise not experienced becomes a fact here. Matters are viewed from new aspects and in new dimensions. It is an experience of entirely new insight, usually occurring when the drug's effects are wearing off. There is some evidence that volunteers in this state are better able to solve certain problems than they otherwise could. However, the statistical evidence for this is not yet complete.

With respect to this experience, undoubtedly LSD does improve learning capacity. Psychopaths, alcoholics and neurotics have in a few moments grasped ideas which had eluded them for years.[12] After the LSD experience the memory of the newly gained insights remains with the subject—a fact which represents one of the main advantages of the experience. However, it must be remembered at the same time that it is often more difficult for the LSD subject to learn more trivial matters. Psychological tests often deal with trivial matters and the LSD subject just cannot be bothered to concern himself with them because he has more interesting transcendental matters to concentrate on. The consequence is that the LSD subject scores poorly in the standard psychological tests. He cannot be bothered with them.

The same principle applies to a sensitivity to art and music. Subjects who, prior to their LSD experience, showed little or no interest in either music or art, gain a lasting appreciation of both, which persists after the experience has worn off. Their eye has learned to see the transcendent and their ear has become accustomed to transcendent melodies. Neither ear nor eye forgets this new aspect, so that the subject has really become enriched with new and valuable artistic insights.[13]

The Aesthetic Experience

Sensory experience is accentuated, with colors becoming more vivid. The blue of the sky becomes of an intensity never before experienced. It is this experience which particularly attracts the younger generation for "kicks," and includes synesthesia, which has already been mentioned. The emotional power behind music and other sensory experience is multiplied, so that the subject will be moved to tears over the slightest pathos, or elevated to hilarity over the slightest gaiety. Artists, poets and others seek this experience.

The Psychedelic Peak, Transcendental or Experimental Mystical Experience

This is one of the experiences which is more difficult to achieve. It resembles the experience of the ancient and modern mystics. More is said of it later (see p.   ). Schizophrenics rarely, if ever, have this experience.[14]

European and other psycholytic therapists have tended to

regard this experience as an unwanted distraction and have discouraged it in their patients. American and Canadian therapists have often reported it. From 3 to 40 percent of patients undergoing LSD therapy have reported a mystical experience, but the incidence and intensity varies according to the dose and the patient's condition and surroundings.

Reports on alcoholics. The following summaries of reports are taken from findings on chronic, hospitalized alcoholics who had received LSD. They had for the most part little interest in religion or mysticism: [15]

> I found myself drifting into another world . . . I saw a gleaming, blinding light with a brilliance no man has ever known. It had no shape nor form, but I *knew* that I was looking at God himself. The magnificence, splendor, and grandeur of this experience cannot be put into words. . . . All the trash and garbage seemed to be washed out of my mind . . . it seemed as if I were born all over again . . . goodness and peace . . . all around me. Words can't describe this. I feel an awe and wonder that such a feeling could have occurred to me . . . a great scene was about to unfold within myself. I actually shook and shuddered at what I felt . . . I . . . saw a glorious beauty of space unfold before me, of light, color, and of song and music . . . of a oneness in fellowship, a wanting to belong to this greatness of beauty and goodness that unfolded before my eyes . . . I could see my family handing me great love. . . . I cried, not bitter tears, but tears of beauty and joy. A beautiful organ was playing . . . it seemed as if angels were singing. All of a sudden I was back in eternity. . . . Peace and happiness, tranquillity. . . . My heart was filled with joy that was overwhelming . . . I felt that time was thousands of years ago, thousands of years from now.
>
> I felt with every sense of my being that I was in hell. My body grew warmer and warmer, then suddenly burst into fire. . . . I lay there and let my body burn up. . . . All at once, after all the doubts and fears, I knew I was a mother and that I loved my child . . . the music playing was 'The Lord's Prayer.' There must have been a short pause in the music but to me it seemed an eternity. I said, 'Don't stop it.

> God is whole in me!' At this point, I felt as if God were holding me in His arms and revealing Himself to me. I smiled and said, 'I've found Him, I've found Him!' I had such a tremendous sense of peace and well being. After so many years of running alone and afraid, God was now with me.[16]

Thus, hearing "The Lord's Prayer" set to music, the expression of God's care over his children in that prayer, was experienced ecstatically by this LSD tripper. But similar accentuations occur with color and taste perception:

> The colors were alive. They glowed. I wanted a purple glass. . . . I wanted to feel the color. I seemed to be one with the soft glowing purple.[17]

> The rose seemed to radiate life. I felt it, smelled it, savored it. I asked for a drink of water and it was nectar. . . . I ate a salami sandwich and relished every bite. I can truthfully say it was the best thing I've ever eaten. . . . I touched the bark of a tree and felt the life running through it feeding the deep green leaves. I touched the grass and it felt like velvet. The soft warm air embraced me. This was life; this was my world and I was at home.[18]

The above patient's Raven I.Q. increased from 94 prior to treatment to 112 after treatment, which may be significant. Also, depression, anxiety and psychotic elements were reduced, although no long-term judgments could be made.

It should not be thought that the experiences of this patient are exceptional. A variety of subjects report that nectarines possessed extreme succulence, water tasted like nectar, timeless worlds without boundaries came into view and were fused with ecstasies of music and unlimited supreme joy. Over against this there are reports of "paying one's taxes"—bad trips. Dr. Kurland points out that LSD therapy plays a role like that of a scalpel in surgery—a really sharp scalpel can be a very useful instrument in the hands of a skillful surgeon, but lethal in other persons' hands. LSD is a very sharp instrument, perhaps the sharpest we possess at the moment, and is therefore potentially very dangerous while remaining potentially very useful.

Overlapping of experiences. It must be borne in mind in interpreting these mystical experiences that the religious and psychotic experiences sometimes overlap. The psychotic subjects sometimes "meet God" and sometimes are "God." And yet the two experiences, although having points in common are by no means identical. This is an area that has not yet been worked out by the psychologists, so new evidence on psychotic and mystical experiences is always welcome. For it is in this very area of mystical and religious experiences that the ferment surrounding LSD is at its hottest. At present there are four "churches" which use the psychedelic/mystical experience as their basis of fellowship—The League for Spiritual Discovery, the Neo-American Church, the Native American Church and the Church of the Awakening.[19]

Analysis of the Mystical Experience

These five basic types of psychedelic experience have been described by Walter N. Pahnke and are generally recognized as belonging to the total LSD experience.[20] The mystical experience is usually classified under eight headings:

1. oneness with the cosmos, or sense of unity with it
2. transcendence of time and space, the subject feeling himself to be outside the three dimensions and time
3. blessedness, peace, love, deepest emotion
4. awe, wonder, humility, reverence, sacredness of the experience
5. new insight into the meaning of life and a new sense of values
6. the paradoxical experience, in which the subject recognizes the identity of opposites
7. the ineffable experience, which is not possible to be communicated by the means of words
8. the experience of transience, which occurs when the main intensity of experience of permanent changes of behavior is taking place and is a result of the LSD mystical experience

To some subjects the mystical experience comes easily, even without drugs. But most have to undergo prolonged mortification of the body and spirit in order to achieve it without drugs. For this reason it has been considered unfair, even almost immoral, for a subject to be able to achieve easily and at will the mystical experience simply by the use of drugs. That is why many initiates feel a hostility to a person or even to a drug which will cheaply and easily let the masses in to an experience which only the elite and the ascetic could achieve and enjoy in days gone by. Derisively the term "instant mysticism" has been coined.[21]

THE IMPORTANCE OF DOSE LEVEL

The differences in the various psychedelic experiences are coupled to some extent to the various dose levels of LSD employed. The general conditions under which ingestion took place and the mood of the subject at the time he took the drug all play a part in the type of experience precipitated. But dosage of LSD does play a critical role in deciding the experience, although it, too, may vary depending on the time interval between the last two LSD doses and the patient's psychological health at the time of the experience.

Varying Experiences

A low dose (below 200 micrograms per adult) gives a high probability of an aesthetic, cognitive or psycholytic experience. A higher dose (200 to 400 micrograms per adult) may give a mystical experience. It should be borne in mind that a psychotic experience may occur at any dose level but is usually more likely to occur at a high-dose level that at a low one. The psychotic experience is the easiest one to produce and the mystical one the most difficult. The setting in which the drug is used, together with the prior mood of the subject, plays a role—as well as the heredity factors which have already been mentioned. Some maintain that about 3 percent of patients treated with LSD experience the mystical phenomenon.

Drug Use for Religious Purposes

The Native American Church, which has cultural connections reaching back to the ages before the birth of Christ, and to the Aztec civilization, has been permitted to use peyote by the Food and Drug Administration and the supreme court of the state of California. However, difficulties have arisen now that Dr. John Aiken, a licensed physician, wishes to use peyote for religious purposes. If the authorities allow the Native American Church to use peyote for religious purposes but refuse a white American licensed physician the same privilege, there would seem to be a clear case of discrimination on the part of United States authorities against white people, allowing them less religious freedom than the native Indians. The authorities in their zeal to protect white people from themselves have maneuvered themselves into a really unenviable position. If drugs were to be outlawed for all religious purposes that fact would be construed as another example of the white man's hegemony over Indians and other minorities who regularly use drugs for religious purposes today and have done so for generations past.

ANALGESIC ACTIVITY OF LSD

LSD was first tried for its analgesic effect by R. Blum and others in 1964.[22] E.C. Kast also reported work on this line using terminal cancer patients.[23] LSD was found to be active and, besides showing an analgesic effect, it reduced the apprehension and fear which are so distressing in these cases. The agony of death and its isolation can be at least partially overcome, both for the patient and the bereaved, by the psychedelic experience. The question would seem to be whether LSD does not also accentuate the experiences of the terminal patient as well as acting as an analgesic with respect to his pain. For even though many subjects experienced pain relief for many hours, they refused to take LSD a second time.[24]

Some people are surprised whenever it is suggested that LSD and similar drugs may have practical applications. The tendency is to regard all "dope" as an unmitigated nuisance. This is, of course, a mistake as the following endeavors to point out.

[1] Abram Hoffer and Humphry Osmond, *The Hallucinogens,* p. 119.

[2] Margaret O. Hyde (ed.), *Mind Drugs,* p. 70.

[3] Hoffer and Osmond, p. 120.

[4] Donald B. Louria, "The Abuse of LSD," in Richard C. DeBold and Russell C. Leaf (eds.), *LSD, Man and Society,* p. 37.

[5] See Sidney Cohen, *The Beyond Within—The LSD Story;* and M. Fink, J. Simeon, W. Hague and T. Itil, "Prolonged Adverse Reactions to LSD in Psychotic Subjects," *Arch. Gen. Psychiat.,* 15 (1966), 450.

[6] Louria, p. 39.

[7] *Ibid.,* p. 50.

[8] The term "psychedelic" was coined by H. Osmond, "A Review of the Effects of Psychotomimetic Agents," *Ann. N.Y. Acad. Sc.,* 66 (1957), 429.

[9] Walter N. Pahnke and W. A. Richards, "Implication of LSD and Experimental Mysticism," *Journal of Religious Health,* 513 (1966), 175.

[10] Walter N. Pahnke, "LSD and Religious Experience," *LSD, Man and Society,* p. 61.

[11] See H. A. Abrahamson (ed.) *The Use of LSD in Psychotherapy and Alcoholism.*

[12] Hoffer and Osmond, *The Hallucinogens,* p. 123.

[13] *Ibid.*

[14] *Ibid.,* pp. 476-77.

[15] Pahnke, *LSD, Man and Society,* pp. 71-72.

[16] A. A. Kurland, *et al.,* "The Therapeutic Potential of LSD in Medicine," *LSD, Man and Society,* p. 26.

[17] *Ibid.,* p. 27.

[18] *Ibid.,* pp. 28-29.

[19] Pahnke, *LSD, Man and Society,* pp. 74-75.

[20] *Ibid.,* pp. 61-64.

[21] Hoffer and Osmond, p. 133.

[22] See R. Blum, *et al., Utopiates: The Use and Users of LSD-25.*

[23] E. C. Kast "A Study of LSD as an Analgesic Agent," *Anaesthesia and Analgesia,* 43 (1964), 285; "LSD and the Dying Patient," *Chicago Medical School Quarterly,* Vol. 26 (1966), No. 2, p. 80; "The Analgesic Action of LSD Compared with Dihydromorphinone and Meperidine," *Bulletin of Drug Addiction and Narcotics,* 27 (1963), 3517; and Blum *et al.*

[24] E. C. Kast and V. J. Collins, "Study of Lysergic Acid Diethylamide as an Analgesic Agent," *Journal of Intern. Anesthet. Res. Soc.,* 43 (1964), 285.

3. Possible Toxicity of and Uses for LSD

POSSIBLE USES FOR LSD

In Chronic Alcoholism

LSD has been used successfully in the treatment of chronic alcoholism. As is well known, the number of cases of chronic alcoholism still nonrelapsed and nonalcoholic after five years' treatment is disappointingly low. Some authorities quote a figure as low as 3 percent of alcoholics nonrelapsed after five years. But using LSD during alcohol withdrawal has given five-year nonrelapsing rates as high as 50 percent. The question is, of course, whether alcoholism is less desirable than LSD!

Mescaline, LSD and psilocybin produce similar experiences, and those natives who used the natural products in their religion knew by experience that they removed the craving for alcohol. Thus the American Indians recognized peyote as a cure for alcoholism.[1] Most workers who have

studied LSD in alcoholism are in agreement with this same
finding for the recent synthetic drug, thus lining up present
experience with the ancient Indian one using natural drugs.
Most modern LSD workers are hopeful of real help against
alcoholism by means of LSD.

To Reduce Intractable Pain

As already mentioned, LSD has been used as an analgesic
to reduce otherwise intractable pain and suffering in terminal
malignant disease. It is known that Aldous Huxley used it in
the last stages of his life when no other alleviation from his
suffering from terminal cancer was possible. The relief from
pain is reported to have been satisfactory.

To Precipitate Schizophrenia

The use of LSD to precipitate a sort of model schizophrenia, which could then be used for drug testing (screen-
ing) has not been successful, since LSD does not precipitate a
real pseudoschizophrenia. If one could "cause" schizophrenia
by giving one drug and then treating it by antischizophrenic
drugs, a useful pharmacological tool would have been won.
But this goal has not been achieved with LSD.

To Aid Clergymen

It is reported that a large number of the clergy in Canada
and England have taken LSD to learn more about psychody-
namics and to revive their feelings for their own religion.[2]
The same source states that ministers have become better
preachers by this means. R. C. Jarman in 1961 published a
sermon entitled "The Most Astounding Experience of My
Life," using his experience of being in heaven or hell as its
subject.[3] He is reported to have found that his preaching
afterward became more effective than it had been for many
years previously. Hoffer and Osmond report that many
psychiatric nurses can and have profited from the LSD
experience, as has been shown in Saskatchewan. In their
experience, and also in the nurses' own opinion, they became

more sympathetic and better nurses as a result of the experience.[4]

TREATMENT FOR LSD POISONING

Physical and Mental Aid

The treatment of LSD intoxication usually involves application of tranquilizers of various potencies, according to the severity of the case, accompanied by psychotherapy. In severe cases electroshock therapy may be required. If the patient has already become psychotic and hospitalized, it is difficult to obtain positive results. The case may be complicated by addiction to other drugs. A dose of nicotinic acid will rapidly end or block the psychedelic experience produced by LSD.

To Forewarn by Education

The general opinion today is that LSD abuse must be educated away. The theory sponsored by many experts is that if one gives people—especially young people—the correct information before they start taking drugs, they will refuse to indulge, even if given the opportunity. Dr. Thadeus Kostrubala of the Stone-Brandel Center said just that in a lecture on LSD given in 1967 before medical sciences students at the University of Illinois Medical Center.

Although it is true that education may serve to keep some people off drugs, the author personally does not see how one can on principle hold to such a general view in the light of past drug experience. The alcoholic usually knows all about alcoholism before he starts drinking. He has usually observed other alcoholics and loathes their addiction. Yet, here, education and loathing of alcoholism are not sufficient to prevent it. If those who personally know the terrors of delirium tremens—a real education—still go on drinking, it would seem that education about other drugs will be insufficient to stop addiction to them too. One might as well hope that sex education before puberty would stop sexual excesses afterward!

It is well known that physicians and nurses are especially exposed to the dangers of drug addiction, with morphine, heroin and cocaine being the drugs often used. No one is better educated than the physician or the nurse before addiction as to the consequences of addiction to these drugs, especially when the subject is tired, depressed and seeks a period of release by a shot of morphine. But even the very special, detailed preaddiction drug education of these professions does not prevent addiction in the professions. It may even, in some cases, help them to become addicted by the very knowledge that the drug will give release from their tensions.

Thus, although education may do something to curb addiction in some subjects, the evidence is that it will by no means stop drug addiction. Addicts are often among the best educated on drugs and their effects both before addiction and afterward. In fact, increasing information on the new drugs seems to be running parallel with increasing addiction and abuse.

THE ECONOMIC SIDE OF LSD TRIPPING

Enormous Profits

A dose for a ten-hour LSD trip may cost anywhere from three to eight dollars, according to the city in which the drug is bought and according to the peddler. The profits associated with LSD sales are enormous when it is remembered that one gram (one million micrograms) may cost between $100 and $500, according to whether it came from London or from New York. If one gram costs $100, 10 micrograms or 10,000 μgms. cost $1, so that 1,000 μgms. cost ten cents and a dose of 100 μgms. will have cost, on this basis, one cent. The LSD subject may thus have to pay $8 for one cent's worth of drug. Such lucrative profits makes the police control of a drug like LSD extremely difficult. Added to this is the ease by which a gram or so of the innocuous-looking white powder can be sent by ordinary airmail letter in thin paper or plastic envelopes. It should be remembered that the LSD peddled in the large cities today may be 90 percent impure, so that doses of 500 to 900 μgms. are necessary for a ten-hour trip. Nobody seems to know much about the possible toxicity of the impurities in LSD sold on the black market, for no one seems to have investigated them.

Americans Spend Millions on Drugs

In order to appreciate the amount of money spent today on obtaining illegal supplies of drugs, it suffices to report that United States narcotic officials estimate that Americans spend $100 million per annum on marijuana alone. San Francisco and Los Angeles each take about 100 kilograms, Boston 200 kilograms and Maine 300 kilograms per weekend. The marijuana is sold in wholesale quantities by dealers in the area and then distributed throughout the respective areas by plane, bus or railway express. A "grass" (marijuana) farmer receives $1 to $2 per kilogram of his product, a town dealer $8 to $10 per kilogram. Retail "grass" costs $55 to $60 per kilogram in Laguna Beach and $90 to $100 per kilogram in San Francisco. In the Midwest the price is $400 per kilogram.

Financial Corruption and Superstition

The financial corruption which accompanies dealing in illicit drugs is enormous. Not only does extortion play its part in extracting the maximum price possible from addicts. Financial corruption and extortion ally themselves rapidly to superstition which, even in our scientific age, is rampant in drug dealing. Astrology, for example, plays a large role and dealers know each other's Zodiac signs. A "Sagittarius" may not wish to do business with a "Pisces." Few deals are clinched until the astrology is in order because the feeling is that if a dealer stops consulting his astrology, sooner or later he is sure to "get busted."

Belief That Few Are Jailed

In addition to these astrological beliefs there remains the

firm conviction in drug-dealing circles that very few people go to jail for selling illegal drugs if they can afford a lawyer. It is, of course, true that a loophole is often available through the mechanism of payoffs, and it is known that police in a number of large cities do take a regular cut from the drug business. Some police authorities even join in a deal, with special lawyers handling the more subtle payoffs:

> One dealer, "busted" in his high-priced apartment, was told by the police which lawyer would handle his case and that the fee would be $20,000. He paid it and went free. . . . "You pay an extortionist's fee to lawyers, but you never come in contact with the person you are paying off. You pay the lawyer, he pays the cops, or the judge or the probationary officer. They arrested me to get all my money. Well, I don't worry about it. It's all part of the game."[5]

One confirmed dealer said, "I like turning people on. It's like preaching religion. I really believe in 'weed'. . . . I don't deal for money. I deal for the enjoyment of seeing people get high. People I don't like I make my money on."[6]

MOTIVATION BEHIND LSD TRIPPING

Frank Barron divides the salient motivation patterns of individuals using or needing LSD as follows:[7]

1. Persons interested in the LSD experience primarily for reasons of aesthetic appreciation or expression. Such individuals enjoy the accentuations of all perception, the increased vividness of color, the change in depth perception, the sharper definition of detail, and change in the time sense. That is, they seek and appreciate the accentuation of whatever experience is occurring. This property may explain the reputed aphrodisiacal (sexual-arousing) properties of the drug. For if a couple takes the drug while really in love with one another, then this experience is likely to be accentuated too, and may lead to an ecstasy of union. But it will, on the other hand, also produce a hell of isolation in a couple taking the drug when they are merely shamming, in other words, it will then prove to be a secondary anaphrodisiac (an agent capable of diminishing sexual desire). Any real experience, delightful or distasteful, will be accentuated. In fact, by this very accentuation of the true state, LSD may disclose to a person who does not really know his own true position just where he really is. "Shamming" may be discovered to the "shammers." This distasteful experience is known as "paying one's taxes." Even such comparatively simple sensory perceptions as those of touch and proprioception may be accentuated to a dramatic degree: "The blanket . . . covering me became alive. I remember touching my face and feeling every particle of my skin. . . . The colors in the room were vibrating and alive."[8]

2. *Persons interested primarily in religious experience.* LSD produces a conception of unity with the universe in which everything appears to be one cosmic process. Its use in religious experience has been discussed.

3. *Persons seeking a cure for alcoholism.* Peyote has long been regarded as a cure for the white man's dipsomania, and LSD has given good results in the same direction, as mentioned by Frank Barron,[9] who attributes the production of the transcendental experience as the most important ingredient in the LSD cure for alcoholism. For alcohol does not only release inhibitions on sexual and aggressive impulses, but produces "meaning contrasts" which may be compared to philosophizing on the meaning of life. Experience with alcoholics often has proved this to be the case.

4. *Persons seeking relief from personal psychological neuroses.* LSD is used in psychological research to uncover repressed memories and for confrontation with real self. Reduction in depression and hypochondria has been shown to occur.

5. *Seriously disturbed persons who need the help of the medically supervised LSD experience to put them on their feet again.*

6. *Chronic social delinquents who wish to escape from themselves.* Here Dr. Barron points out that LSD is not a

dangerous drug in the sense that thalidomide, heroin, methyl alcohol or tobacco are dangerous.[10] But LSD is dangerous when used by the dangerous delinquent.

7. *Psychiatric nurses and psychiatrists have sought the LSD experience in the hope that they will thereby better understand their patients.* Some preachers have done the same in the hope of experiencing heaven and hell.[11]

PREDICTION OF LSD REACTIONS (BAD TRIPS)

Are there any means available for predicting beforehand whether a particular individual is likely to react badly to LSD or other hallucinogens? As already pointed out, unstable persons or those with a tendency to incipient schizophrenia are likely to react badly. The question is whether there are means available of recognizing such persons by means of objective tests carried out before treatment with the hallucinogen.

The majority of untreated schizophrenics excrete a substance in their urine which stains mauve when treated with Ehrlich's reagent on paper chromatograms.[12] When such patients recover from their schizophrenia the mauve staining substance ceases to be excreted. Hoffer and Osmond designated persons excreting this mauve staining factor as "malvarians."[13]

Since malvarians biochemically resemble the majority of schizophrenics, Hoffer is of the opinion that malvarians, who are often clearly schizophrenic, would probably react badly to LSD or other hallucinogens. It would appear that this is, in fact, the case.

Early tests on this basis showed that none of the nonmalvarians suffered from prolonged reactions to LSD, whereas four out of twenty malvarians who were not overt schizophrenics did suffer such reactions for a week or longer. Thus, by not giving LSD to malvarians, one reduces the risk of bad LSD trips.

It is interesting to note in this connection that some LSD subjects showed transient malvaria after LSD for up to twenty-four hours and that such subjects experienced bad trips after subsequent LSD treatment.

TRANSFER OF A PSYCHOTIC INTO A TRANSCENDENTAL EXPERIENCE

Need for Controlled Surroundings

To carry through a psychedelic experience safely and productively, the surroundings in which it takes place must be carefully controlled. The whole experience can be greatly modified by the setting as well as by the patient, his psychological condition and makeup and the dose of LSD given. If a psychedelic experience is desired, great care should be taken to ensure the personal comfort of the subject and to avoid noisy rooms and unsuitable furnishings. Even such matters as architecture can be of decisive importance.

The number of people present at the experience is also of profound importance. It has been found that, for therapeutic purposes, two to four people may with advantage be present. All the observers should be present in the room before the experience begins, because coming and going, especially of strangers, can be profoundly deleterious to the LSD experience. [14]

Music, harmonious decor and tasteful paintings can all help the subject toward the desired psychedelic experience. Patients frozen in a psychotomimetic experience can be transferred rapidly—within a few seconds—into a satisfactory psychedelic experience by playing music which has pleasant associations for them. On the other hand, some subjects find all music intolerable and are not helped by visual aids. Attempts to impose a structure onto the experience by means of interviews and various props may radically alter the whole experience.

Uses Sense-Perception Mechanisms

As already pointed out, the LSD experience works through the ordinary sense-perception mechanisms. For example, normal subjects treated with LSD see colors, lights, jewels, cathedrals, patterns, etc., even when their eyes are blind-folded, whereas subjects blind from birth report no visual reaction under LSD.[15] Blind subjects who have to some extent overcome blindness by compensatory auditory acuity, experience LSD in the realm of sound. Hoffer and Osmond report that the room pulsated and the ceiling lowered itself for such subjects.[16] One blind patient did, however, report "seeing" a flash of light. The same authors report that sensory deprivation for persons confined in light-proof, sound-attenuated cubicles for two hours, antagonized the LSD experience.[17] As soon as the sensory deprivation was interrupted, the LSD experience imposed itself in a sudden rush of visual experiences.

These findings in the blind and in those persons under-going sensory deprivation would seem to support once more the hypothesis of the mechanism of LSD action which we have already mentioned, namely, that LSD alters the recep-tion of sensory-perception stimuli as they come into the brain's processing and decoding centers. But, of course, an *alteration* in perception can only be noticed when some perception is actually taking place. In blindness no visual perception, as such, is present; therefore, no visual experience can be present. Similarly, in the light-proof and sound-atten-uated cubicles, perception is much reduced, with corres-ponding reduction of alteration of perception. Persons blindfolded or undergoing other kinds of sensory deprivation have few sensory impulses to process, so that LSD influence on nonfunctional processes does not make itself so notice-ably felt.

An excellent guide to the total recent literature on psyche-delic drugs has been compiled in Charles E. Tart's book.[18]

[1] Abram Hoffer and Humphry Osmond, *The Hallucinogens,* p. 155.
[1a] Charles E. Tart (ed.), *Altered States of Consciousness,* pp. 441-443.
[2] *Ibid.,* p. 235.
[3] R. C. Jarman, "The Most Astounding Experience of My Life" (sermon), *Chapel Bells* (1961).
[4] Hoffer and Osmond, p. 234. Cf. article by W. B. Bolton in *Canadian Journal of Occupational Therapy,* 281 (1961), 55.

[5]*Look* magazine (Mar. 5, 1968), p. 59.

[6]*Ibid.*

[7]Frank Barron, "Motivational Patterns in LSD Usage" in Richard C. DeBold and Russell C. Leaf (eds.), *LSD, Man and Society,* p. 9.

[8]A. A. Kurland, *et al.,* "The Therapeutic Potential of LSD in Medicine," *LSD, Man . . . ,* pp. 25-26.

[9]Barron, *ibid.*

[10]*Ibid.*

[11]Hoffer and Osmond, pp. 231, 235.

[12]See D. Irvine, "Apparently Non-idolic Ehrlich-Positive Substances Related to Mental Illness," *Journal of Neuropsychiatry,* 2 (1961), 292; and Hoffer and Osmond, "A Card Sorting Test Helpful in Making Psychiatric Diagnosis" and "The Relationship Between an Unknown Factor ('US') in Urine of Subjects and Hod Test Results," *Journal of Neuropsychiatry,* 2 (1961), 306, 363; "The Association Between Schizophrenia and Two Objective Tests," *Canadian Medical Association Journal,* 87 (1962), 641.

[13]Hoffer and Osmond, "Malvaria: A New Psychiatric Disease," *Acta Psychiatria Scandinavica,* 39 (1963), 335; "Some Problems of Stochastic Psychiatry," *Journal of Neuropsychiatry,* 5 (1964), 97.

[14]Hoffer and Osmond, *The Hallucinogens,* p. 112.

[15]*Ibid.,* p. 115.

[16]*Ibid.,* p. 116.

[17]*Ibid.*

[18]Charles E. Tart (ed.), *Altered States of Consciousness,* pp. 477-483.

4. Properties of Marijuana and Hashish (Cannabis Drugs)

HASHISH AND MARIJUANA

A Description of Cannabis Drugs

No account of psychopharmacologically active drugs would be complete without a description of the active agents derived from the hemp plant *Cannabis sativa L.* and generally known in the United States as marijuana (or marihuana).

In various countries. In India there are three grades of cannabis. They are *bhang,* which is cheap and low in potency and is ingested as a drink; *ganja,* which is two or three times as strong as *bhang;* and *charas,* which is the unadulterated resin from the plant or dried flower. Smoking is the common mode of consumption for *ganja* and *charas.* In Morocco cannabis preparations are known as *kif.* In South America a similar preparation is known as *dagga.*[1]

The term "hashish" is used for a powdered and sifted form of charas. United States marijuana is about one-fifth to one-eighth as potent as the Indian charas resin. An active ingredient of all these cannabis preparations is tetrahydro-cannabinol, which has been synthesized and tested pharma-cologically.

The "American type" of marijuana is a mixture found on the illicit drug market and is, as already pointed out, of lower grade than hashish, which is derived from the same plant. Hashish may be some five to eight times more potent than marijuana and is widely used in some Eastern countries for smoking purposes. Nearly all the active resin in *Cannabis sativa L.* is concentrated in the flowering tops of the female plant, of which hashish largely consists. In American mari-juana are found leaves, seeds, stems and tops, which accounts for the lower potency of marijuana compared with hashish. Marijuana is commonly called "grass," "weed," "pot" or "muggles" by users. Smoking hashish with its higher potency can be a good deal more dangerous than smoking marijuana.

Legalization Suggested

Perhaps because marijuana is considered to be the safest of the hallucinogens it has been suggested that its use should be legalized. Demands in this direction have been made, notably in England.[2]

One of the characteristic effects produced by marijuana is its tendency to produce feelings of omnipotence and superi-ority in the smoker—a fact which can make the drug a bad risk in car drivers who are habitués. All the same, there is little evidence connecting marijuana use with criminality or psychosis as such.[3]

It should be remembered that in the United States the Marijuana Tax Act of 1937 places the same type of controls on the use of marijuana as the Harrison Narcotic Act of 1914 placed on narcotic drugs.[4] But marijuana is not considered to be a narcotic from the point of view of federal law though state laws define it as a narcotic. These are only points of law, but it is important to remember that the drug is controlled by law and that its abuse is punishable as a felony.

The question naturally arises as to why marijuana should be classed as a socially unacceptable drug. Many people have smoked marijuana cigarettes ("reefers") for long periods with apparently no more, and perhaps less, harm than that entailed by smoking tobacco or by drinking the regular glass of wine or whisky. Why legalize alcohol and tobacco while enforcing a kind of prohibition against the active substances derived from hemp?

Results of Using Hashish

There is no doubt today about the fact that refined hashish is a much more potent hallucinogen than the mild marijuana available currently in the United States. The chronic use of refined hashish in Egypt, for example, is reported to have brought about a high incidence of overt insanity.[5] In India, where chronic hashish abuse is common, evidence of damaged health is reported to have been found in 42 percent of the chronic abusers.[6] The press reports that in Egypt, where some 30 percent of the population is habituated to the smoking of refined hashish, there is said to be evidence that the habit is accompanied by brain-cell damage, violence and murder. The opinion of some experts is that the use of the drug is vicious, of no medical value and that it has earned nothing but odium and contempt.[7] Norman Taylor, an opponent of narcotic prohibitive restrictions, admits that refined hashish is so potent that its continued use leads "straight to the lunatic asylum."[8]

Sections of the United States press have given publicity recently to the view that there may be no direct connection between the abuse of marijuana and crime. Facts and figures cited often seem to bear out this view. But some observers report a relationship in other countries between crime and the abuse of hashish. And in New Orleans it has been shown that among major criminals there a high percentage do smoke marijuana. This does not necessarily prove a causal relationship between criminality and cannabis smoking; but although marijuana will not necessarily precipitate crime in normal individuals, it may be potent enough to bring out criminality in those who have a predisposition toward crime.

Where Can the Line Be Drawn?

The problem of the status of marijuana in producing antisocial behavior resolves itself into the problem of drawing the line between hallucinatory and nonhallucinatory drugs. The marijuana available in the United States is so diluted with nonactive parts of *Cannabis sativa L.* that many individuals can, in fact, use it with comparative impunity. Little or no antisocial behavior develops. Hashish, on the other hand, derived and refined from the same plant source, is often so potent that it has the reputation of inducing acts of violence and murder. Some experts believe that marijuana affects only the most susceptible in an antisocial manner.

Since there is only a difference of potency between hashish and marijuana, where can the legislature draw the line of demarcation? If marijuana were not rigorously restricted, the potent, purified tetrahydrocannabinols could be extracted from it and used for narcotic purposes in just the same way that heroin and morphine would become available if opium were freely available to all. If the comparatively innocuous marijuana were freed, more concentrated forms would quickly be manufactured, with the accompanying antisocial behavior said to be produced by hashish smoking. This is the "official" position.

For this reason the Uniform Narcotic Drug Act, in one form of legislation or another, is in force throughout the United States and prohibits any person from manufacturing, possessing, selling, purchasing, prescribing, administering or giving away any narcotic drug, except as authorized by the act. The importation of crude drugs, except for the limited quantities of crude opium and coca leaves necessary for the manufacture of medical supplies, is prohibited. Opium importation for smoking is specifically banned, as is also the importation of opium intended for the manufacture of heroin.

ACTIVE PRINCIPLES

The active principle of marijuana resides mostly in its tetrahydrocannabinol content. The tetrahydrocannabinols are powerful compounds when used in doses sufficient to produce intoxication. They possess antibacterial, analgesic, anticonvulsive and local anesthetic properties.[9] However, in the resin derived from the plant there exist a number of other potent drugs besides the tetrahydrocannabinols. The totality of these active agents produce hilarity, carelessness, loquacious euphoria, distortion and impairment of perception and judgment, irritability and confusion. Over and above these effects, the sensory threshold to optical and acoustical stimuli is lowered. That is, the smoker becomes increasingly sensitive to light and sound stimuli. Aggressiveness and sleep disturbances follow the use of hashish. [10]

G. M. Carstairs described the following effects as manifesting themselves after the administration of bhang in Indian Brahmins:[11]

1. A transient euphoria with feeling of superiority and superhuman insight.
2. Sensory hyperesthesia, sights and sounds becoming vivid and meaningful.
3. Distortion of sense of time and space.
4. Loss of judgment.
5. Exaggeration of both sympathy and antipathy.
6. *"El Kif"* or "blessed repose" during which the will to act is destroyed. This state is also known as that of oneiritic ecstasy.
7. After some hours of the trancelike state, sleep supervenes.

In the United Kingdom today it would seem that the use of hashish has ousted the use of marijuana, although the strength of the material referred to as hashish there is not always certain. [12]

ABSTINENCE

Abstinence from marijuana does not produce a typical

physiological withdrawal syndrome, such as occurs on withdrawing heroin. This means that true addiction—in the sense that morphine and heroin produce addiction—does not occur in the abuse of marijuana. But psychological dependence on marijuana is said by some to drive the chronic user to great lengths to ensure himself a supply of the drug. Others doubt this view. Deprivation may apparently produce anxiety, malaise and depression with suicidal tendencies. Thus marijuana is said by some to be habituating rather than addicting. Others maintain that there is not even habituation. It must be clearly understood that marijuana smoking must be *learned* before its physiological effects are experienced.[13]

The physiological effects of marijuana intoxication include loss of limb coordination (ataxia); reduced blood-sugar concentration (hypoglycemia); increased appetite, especially for sugar-containing foods; lowered body temperature (hypothermia); and inflammation of the mucous membranes of the mouth, pharynx and bronchial tubes. Many claim that the hallucinatory properties of marijuana and LSD are closely related.[14]

CURRENT RESEARCH AND OBSERVATION

Disturbances from Hashish

A CIBA Foundation report summarizes much of the current research on this topic in the following terms: "It is well known that taking hashish causes both pathological and psychic disturbances, thus rendering the addict a burden to society."[15] If this view is correct, it is reasonable that the worldwide use of hashish should be prohibited by law under the Single Convention on Narcotic Drugs of 1961. The rationale lying behind this prohibition is twofold: the harmful effect of the drug on the consumer and the antisocial behavior it produces.

The finding is supported by Professor C. G. Gardibkas' work on hashish-smoking individuals.[16] In a group of 379 criminals Dr. Gardibkas found that 117 of them became criminally inclined only after habituation to hashish. The function of hashish seems to reside in its capacity to bolster courage to commit aggressive acts. The mental confusion resulting from hashish intoxication also aids in crime. Since muscular incoordination does not occur so rapidly under the influence of hashish as it does under alcoholic intoxication, the hashish criminal possesses the strength, coordination and skill to carry out his crime, whereas the alcoholic criminal would not succeed because of muscular incoordination.[17]

Although marijuana smoking does not produce ataxia as quickly as alcohol, yet it does, in spite of what we have said above, render its user less capable of carrying through highly complex tasks, such as driving a car. There is some evidence that cannabis smoking has been the cause of increased traffic accidents in Mexico, Cuba and other countries.[18]

Use of One Drug Leads to Another

At this point it should be remembered that the use of one drug may, in itself, be comparatively harmless. Experience has shown, however, that the use of one drug very often leads to the use of a second and possibly more dangerous drug. Thus the user of a relatively harmless drug may "graduate" to a more potent and destructive narcotic. Some maintain that this is the case with marijuana, but many deny this position. Marijuana users are said by some to graduate to something more potent as their drug needs rise with time. This apparent tendency to graduate from marijuana to the strongest opiates, such as heroin and morphine, has been discussed worldwide by narcotic experts.

The actual symptoms and experiences of narcotics of the marijuana class are mentioned in the Introduction, where it is pointed out that the ancient Chinese Emperor Shen Nung (2700 B.C.) was well acquainted with the exact toxic manifestations of *Cannabis sativa* intoxication.

Decreased or Increased Usage?

Although marijuana smoking makes headlines in the

United States, some authorities believe that its use may be on the wane. The reasons given are simple. It is bulky to transport, so that detection is relatively easy. Its abuse carries with it the penalty of a felony, whereas the abuse of amphetamines carries the milder penalty resulting from a misdemeanor. Amphetamines, in the view of these authorities, are taking the place of marijuana since they are easier to ship undetected, besides being easily synthesized in any moderately well-equipped laboratory. LSD is, of course, the most difficult substance to detect and prohibit because of its exceedingly high potency and the consequent low-dose level required to produce its effect.

Over against these views other authorities believe the opposite state of affairs to be the case, and maintain that marijuana abuse is on the increase and LSD usage on the decrease. Dana L. Farnsworth of Harvard estimates that 30 to 35 percent of the students at major universities on the East and West coasts have tried marijuana at least once. Half of them did not repeat the experiment. Farnsworth estimated that 5 percent of the students had tried LSD at the height of its popularity several years ago and that current use was under 1 percent. This decline is reputed to be due to the knowledge students now have of the toxic properties of LSD, particularly those causing chromosomal damage,[19] together with the permanent and serious psychoses its use may precipitate.

Since there seems to be a good deal of overstatement with regard to the toxicity and possible undesirability of marijuana use, information is given here which has been supplied by official investigations in this area.

OFFICIAL REPORTS

Indian Hemp Drug Commission

The Indian Hemp Drug Commission stated:

> It has been clearly established that the occasional use of hemp in moderate doses may be beneficial; but this use

may be regarded as medicinal in character. . . . In regard to the physical effects, the Commission have come to the conclusion that the moderate use of hemp drugs is practically attended by no evil results at all. There may be exceptional cases in which, owing to idiosyncrasies of constitution, the drugs in even moderate use may be injurious.

In respect to the alleged mental effects of the drugs, the Commission have come to the conclusion that the moderate use of hemp drugs produces no injurious effects on the mind.

In regard to the moral effects of the drugs, the Commission are of the opinion that their moderate use produces no moral injury whatever. There is no adequate ground for believing that it injuriously affects the character of the consumer. . . . For all practical purposes it may be laid down that there is little or no connection between the use of hemp drugs or crime.

Viewing the subject generally, it may be added that the moderate use of these drugs is the rule, and that the excessive use is comparatively exceptional.[20]

Panama Canal Zone Governor's Committee

The Panama Canal Zone Governor's Committee of April—December, 1925, gave the following evidence on marijuana:

There is no evidence that marijuana as grown here is a "habit forming" drug in the sense in which the term is applied to alcohol, opium, cocaine, etc., or that it has any appreciably deleterious influence on the individual using it. . . . Delinquencies due to marijuana smoking are negligible in number when compared with delinquencies resulting from the use of alcoholic drinks.[21]

White House Conference

The proceedings of the White House Conference on Narcotic and Drug Abuse, held September 27-28, 1962, in Washington, D.C., state:

It is the opinion of the Panel that the hazards of Marijuana *per se* have been exaggerated and that long criminal sentences imposed on an occasional user or possessor of the drug are in poor social perspective. Although Marijuana has long held the reputation of inciting individuals to commit sexual offenses and other antisocial acts, the evidence is inadequate to substantiate this. Tolerance and physical dependence do not develop and withdrawal does not produce an abstinence syndrome.[22]

New York Academy of Medicine Report

A complete study of the marijuana problem was undertaken by the New York Academy of Medicine at the request of Mayor Fiorello H. LaGuardia.[23] The report of the commission appointed was issued in 1944 and comprised an exhaustive medical and sociological analysis of the use of marijuana in New York. Its authors were expert medical practitioners.

Significantly enough, the mayor's report came to substantially the same conclusions as those reached some fifty years previously by the Indian Hemp Drug Commission mentioned above. The main conclusions reached by the academy are:

1. Marijuana is used extensively in the borough of Manhattan, but the problem is not as acute as it is reported to be in other sections of the United States.
2. The introduction of marijuana into this area is recent as compared to other localities.
3. The cost of marijuana is low and therefore within the purchasing power of most persons.
4. The distribution and use of marijuana is centered in Harlem.
5. The majority of marijuana smokers are Negroes and Latin-Americans.
6. The consensus among marijuana smokers is that the use of the drug creates a certain feeling of adequacy.
7. The practice of smoking marijuana does not lead to addiction in the medical sense of the word.
8. The sale and distribution of marijuana is not under the control of any single organized group.

9. The use of marijuana does not lead to morphine or heroin or cocaine addiction and no effort is made to create a market for those narcotics by stimulating the practice of marijuana smoking.
10. Marijuana is not the determining factor in the commission of major crimes.
11. Marijuana smoking is not widespread among schoolchildren.
12. Juvenile delinquency is not associated with the practice of smoking marijuana.
13. The publicity concerning the catastrophic effects of marijuana smoking in New York is unfounded.[24]

The experts appointed to the mayor's commission reported further that the use of marijuana was not linked to sexuality, nor was its use connected with major crime, for the professional criminal would usually not associate with marijuana smokers.[25] They also reported that infrequent or even constant use of marijuana did not result in physical or mental deterioration.[26] The confirmed marijuana smoker may consume from six to ten cigarettes daily. He seems to know just how much he needs to become "high" on marijuana, but sweet wines are reputed to increase the effect of marijuana. Another point confirmed by the commission was that marijuana smokers derive greater pleasure from smoking in the company of other smokers. They share and puff at each other's cigarettes. The whole atmosphere is that of a congenial social club, with any rowdiness immediately suppressed and the offenders ejected summarily. Pup tents were often set up on Harlem rooftops in which they smoked their cigarettes and then emerged to admire the sky and the stars when the drug had taken effect.

TOXIC EFFECTS

Among some of the main confirmed toxic effects of marijuana smoking may be mentioned some pupil dilation, dryness of the mouth, dizziness and nausea, restlessness, together with conjunctivitis (inflammation of the eye membranes), which some 72 percent of cannabis smokers suffered from. In fact, some investigators have used this symptom as a means of detecting cannabis smoking. Where hashish has been used, it has been reported that cannabis psychosis is common. Some 30 to 50 percent of hospitalized mental cases were classed as cannabis psychosis. Others state that no characteristic cannabis psychosis exists and that not even marijuana will produce *de novo* a psychosis in a well-integrated stable person.[27]

CANNABIS HALLUCINATIONS

Since in 1951 there were some two hundred million cannabis users throughout the world (more numerous than members of the Jewish and Protestant faiths combined), a word on the actual hallucinatory properties of cannabis, as taken from case reports, will be in order.[28]

> It was too much, like I only make about four pokes, and I couldn't even get it out of my mouth, I was so high, and I got real flipped. In the basement you know, I just couldn't stay in there anymore. My heart was pounding . . . and I was going out of my mind; I thought I was losing my mind completely. . . . I walked outside, and it was 5° below zero, and I thought I was dying, and I had my coat open; I was sweating, I was perspiring . . . and I fainted behind a bush. I don't know how long I laid there. I woke up and I was feeling the worst. . . . So then all weekend I started flipping, seeing things there and just going through hell. . . . I just quit for a long time then.
>
> In the earliest stages of intoxication the will power is destroyed and inhibitions and restraints are released; the moral barricades are broken down and often debauchery and sexuality result. When mental instability is inherent, the behavior is generally violent. An egotist will enjoy delusions of grandeur, the timid individual will suffer anxiety, and the aggressive one often will resort to acts of violence and crime. Dormant tendencies are released and while the subject may know what is happening, he has become powerless to prevent it. Constant use produces an

incapacity for work and a disorientation of purpose.

I have had some that made me feel like very invigorated and also it gives a very strong appetite . . . that's probably good for some people who are underweight. [29]

The first quotation shows how a bad marijuana trip can look to the inexperienced. The second quotation shows how much drug action depends on the type of individual who is taking it. Marijuana and hashish can be dangerous in certain persons, but are relatively harmless in well-integrated individuals.

Stimulate Nervous System

In general it can be said that alcohol and amphetamines stimulate the efferent nervous system, thus leading to muscular and other stimulation. On the other hand, the psychedelic drugs, including marijuana, stimulate the afferent nervous system, increasing meditation, sensual openness and artistic and religious preoccupation. In line with this emphasis, cannabis is known to amplify the sense of touch, which would explain its reported aphrodisiac properties. [30] Such properties are often referred to by adepts as a well-kept marijuana secret.

Marijuana has weak but definite psychedelic properties, which are well brought out in the following quotation:

Marijuana is the mildest of the psychedelic drugs. . . . Experienced marijuana users know how easy it is to "hang some one up" on the gustatory sense by talking about food during a session. Pot-smoking artists turn off visual symbols. [31]

The following reports were written as a result of hashish ingestion:

Solitude reigned in the drawing room. . . . All of a sudden a red flash passed beneath my eyelids, innumerable candles burst into light and I felt bathed in a warm, clear glow. I was indeed in the same place, but it was as different as a sketch from a painting: everything was larger, richer, more gorgeous. Reality served as a point of departure for the splendors of the hallucination. . . . An enigmatic character suddenly appeared before me. How had he come it? I cannot say; yet the sight of him caused me no alarm. His nose was carved like a bird's beak; his green eyes, which he frequently wiped with an immense handkerchief, were encircled with three brown rings. . . . His legs, I must confess, were made of a bifurcated mandrake root—black, rough, full of knots and bulges—which seemed to have been freshly picked, for clods of earth still clung to its filaments. These legs thrummed and twisted with extraordinary activity. . . . The strange character burst into sobs, wiped his eyes with a sweeping gesture and said in the most mournful tones: "It is today that we must die laughing." Tears as large as peas rolled across the wings of his nose. "Laughing. . . . laughing. . . ." repeated a choir of echo-like, discordant nasal voices. . . . Little by little, the drawing room became filled with extraordinary figures. . . . With each new apparition, a Homeric, Olympian, immense, dumbfounding laugh, which seemed to resound through infinity, burst about me with a thunderous roar. . . . No, it's too funny; no more. . . . funnier and funnier. . . . enough, I can bear no more. . . . stop, I'm stifling! I'm choking! Don't look at me so. . . . or place hoops about me, I'm going to burst. . . . Despite these half jesting, half entreating protestations, the awesome hilarity went ever increasing, the din grew in intensity, the floors and walls of the house heaved and palpitated like a human diaphragm, shaken by the frenetic, irresistible, implacable laughter. . . . "My God, how happy I am!" "What felicity!" "I am swimming in ecstasy!" "I am in Paradise!" "I am diving into abysses of delight!" [32]

Time Reversal

The marijuana experience produces an interference with the time sense, just as can occur under the influence of LSD:

I made the journey four or five hundred times to interrogate the clock face with a horrible anxiety. . . . The hands did not move. "Wretch! You have stopped the pendulum," I cried, drunken with rage. "I have not, it is going back and forth as usual. . . . but suns will crumble into dust before yon steel arrow advances a millionth of one millimeter." "Time has risen from the dead," shouted happy, childish voices. "Now go see the clock!" The hands pointed to eleven o'clock. "Sir, your carriage is downstairs," said a servant. The dream was at an end. . . . my reason had returned. [33]

Intoxication Phases

The hashish type of intoxication falls into three successive phases. The first phase, which is often slow in setting in and which makes the novice impatient, consists of a sort of irrelevant and irresistible hilarity. Simple words, trivial ideas are seen in a compellingly comical light. Adepts say that this hilarity is as irresistible and painful as a tickle.[34] "Self control, good sense and orderly thoughts of a prudent observer, who has abstained from intoxication—these delight and amuse you like a dementia. Your roles are inverted: his calmness drives you to extremes of ironic disdain."[35]

After the laughter and mirth of the first stage, there usually follows a lull. The second stage is preceded by a chilliness in the extremities and a weakness of the arms and legs. Then the eyes feel as if they were bulging under the weight of ecstasy which floods in and causes the lips to feel as if they were shrinking and as if the gullet were constricted. Sighs and groans may accompany this second stage. A new subtlety and sensory acuity show themselves in the senses of smell, sight, hearing and touch. The eyes may have the illusion of beholding the infinite, and the ear becomes able to pick out certain sounds even in the midst of a din.

It is at this stage that the hallucinations proper set in. Objects acquire new and strange appearances as they become distorted and transformed. Transposition of ideas occurs. Synesthesia may be experienced as sounds become clothed in color, and colors may contain music. Objects such as trees become endowed with the hashish adept's passions, desires and feelings. As the tree groans and sways in the wind, it becomes so loaded with the adept's own feelings that he, the person, becomes the tree. In the same way, as the adept observes and hears the joyful song of the soaring lark, he becomes the lark.

The third stage sets in as the psychedelic effect of the drug begins to wear off and periods of drug experience begin to alternate with periods in which nothing particular happens.

May Precipitate Psychosis

In some cases the effects of hashish or marijuana ingestion do not wear off so easily as to disappear without trace. Sometimes a definite psychosis may be precipitated, but this usually occurs only when there is a patient predisposition to psychosis, although there are exceptions to this. Thus a previous history of epilepsy or serious drug addiction may predispose to psychosis after cannabis ingestion. Previous heroin addiction may be a case in point. "Prison psychosis" may also predispose to toxic reactions after the use of cannabis.[36] However, as is so often the case in neuropharmacology, well-integrated individuals do not usually show these toxic effects (there are notable exceptions) and no mental deterioration is to be expected from repeated use of moderate doses of the cannabis drugs.[37] This is particularly true of marijuana, which, in general, would appear to be less dangerous than alcohol. It is generally recognized that marijuana and the pop-jazz culture belong together today.[38]

Whatever the legal rights and wrongs, the use of marijuana is certainly not considered to be either dangerous or a criminal form of behavior among adolescents today. Many justify its use on the basis that it is preferable to alcohol abuse. From the point of view of health or addiction it is considered to be harmless.[39]

It is often maintained by drug officialdom that a major danger of marijuana lies in the tendency it produces of leading its abusers on to heroin and other so-called hard drugs. Dr. Louria, who is one of today's leading experts on addiction, says, "One point is worthy of emphasis regarding marijuana and heroin. I think we have the answer to the question—'Does marijuana lead to heroin'; the answer is unequivocally 'No'. There is no other conclusion one can draw from the large number of college students involved with marijuana and the relatively few using heroin. . . . It is very rare to find heroin abuse in American colleges; consequently I do not think that marijuana use does result in abuse of hard core drugs such as heroin."[40] On the other hand, if a person begins to experiment with any type of drug on himself, he may graduate to more powerful drugs, but this tendency has little to do with the pharmacology of the first drug he uses.

CATARIA

One of the latest of the hallucinatory drugs is the plant known as *Cataria* or catnip. This plant is related to the mint family. In its dried form it is already on the market and is being widely used. So far it has not been declared illegal and anyone can buy it by mail order at $2.50 per lid or six lids for $10.00.

Starsin Catarias, a drug company operating from Inglewood, California, is supplying the dried active parts of this plant and instructions for its use. On receipt of the money the following information is sent out:

> Enclosed is your order of Starsin Catarias and with it all time coming should be anticipated. Nothing can be a surprise and all that startles is relative to potential maturity. Wisdom should not tolerate neglect, but quantity is harmless so first enjoy and later value discipline.
>
> Starsin Catarias should be rolled in regular cigarette papers and after inhaling the fumes should be held in the lungs until absorbed. Non-smokers will note more of a problem here since inhaling is often the salient aspect of getting high. Always be confident, however, that Starsin Catarias is completely harmless and requires no more caution than tobacco.
>
> Surround yourself with that which you love and are pleased by: music, books, objects of sexual enlightenment.
>
> As long as we are legally permitted to continue we shall make Starsin Catarias available at the same price. To be stoned, to be blessed, to be high, to be God, with God, without it, without Him, one, to be high.

76

Cataria is a good deal less active than marijuana as an hallucinatory agent. But apparently it is desirable because it induces auditory hallucination, whereas marijuana is especially active in the visual field.[41] Thus music is supposed to be particularly appreciated under *Cataria*.

[1] David Solomon, *The Marihuana Papers,* p. 402.

[2] Donald B. Louria, "Abuse of Lysergic Acid Diethylamide," in C. W. M. Wilson (ed.), *Adolescent Drug Dependence,* p. 88.

[3] *Ibid.,* p. 89; and C.W.M. Wilson and Arnold Linken, "The Use of Cannabis, " *ibid.,* p. 110.

[4] Donald E. Miller, *Narcotic Drug and Marijuana Controls,* National Association of Student Personnel Administrators, Drug Education Project, 1966-67.

[5] Robert S. DeRopp, *Drugs and the Mind,* p. 97, see also Erich Hesse, *Narcotics and Drug Addiction,* p. 93.

[6] DeRopp, p. 98.

[7] Murray E. Jarvik, "Drugs Used in the Treatment of Psychiatric Disorders," in Louis S. Goodman and Alfred Gilman (eds.), *The Pharmacological Basis of Therapeutics,* p. 174.

[8] Norman Taylor, *Narcotics, Nature's Dangerous Gift,* p. 15.

[9] K. L. Stuart, "Ganja/Cannabis sativa L.," (review), *W. L. Med. J.,* 12 (1963) 159.

[10] N. Eddy, H. Halbach, H. Isbell, M. H. Seevers, *Drug Dependence: Its Significance and Characteristics,* Bulletin of World Health Organization, pp. 728-29.

[11] G. M. Carstairs,"Daru and Bhang," *Quarterly Journal of Studies on Alcohol* 15 (1954), 220-37; see also Wilson and Linken, pp. 110, 118.

[12] Wilson and Linken, p. 115.

[13] See "Medicine," *Time* (Dec. 20, 1968).

[14] Donald B. Louria and M. Sokolow, *Nightmare Drugs,* p. 32.

[15] G. Joachimoglu, "Natural and Smoked Hashish," CIBA Foundation Study Group No. 21, *Hashish, Its Chemistry and Pharmacology* (1965), p. 5.

[16] C. G. Gardibkas, *Hashish and Crime,* p. 5.

[17] David W. Maurer and Victor H. Vogel, *Narcotics and Narcotic Addiction,* p. 245.

[18] See United Nations Document E/CN 7/1 268 (May 14, 1965), statement by the French Delegation; and *Effects of the Use and Abuse of Narcotic Drugs on Accidents in General and on Road Accidents in Particular,* United Nations Document E/CN 7/481 (Sept. 14, 1965).

[19] Philip H. Alselson, editorial, *Science,* Vol. 159 (Mar. 15, 1968), No. 3820. See also R. C. DeBold and R. C. Leaf (eds.), *LSD, Man and Society.*

[20] *Report of Indian Hemp Drug Commission,* 1893-94, pp. 262-64, as cited by Solomon, p, 192.

[21] *The Military Surgeon,* Journal of the Association of Military Surgeons of the USA (Nov., 1933), p. 274, as cited by Solomon, p. 192.

[22] *The Proceedings of the White House Conference on Narcotic and Drug Abuse* (Sept., 1962), p. 286, as cited by Solomon, p. 193.

[23] Solomon, pp. 232-312.

[24] As cited by *ibid.*, pp. 259-60; details of the report are given on pp. 232-312.
[25] Cf. Mayor LaGuardia's report as cited by Solomon, pp. 250-51.
[26] *Ibid.*, pp. 248-49.
[27] *Ibid.*, pp. 410-11.
[28] *United Nations Report on Cannabis* as cited by *ibid.*, pp. 86-87.
[29] Solomon, pp. 44-45, 54-55, 56.
[30] *Ibid.*, p. 96.
[31] *Ibid.*
[32] *Ibid.*, pp. 126-29.
[33] *Ibid.*, p. 134.
[34] *Ibid.*, p. 139.
[35] *Ibid.*
[36] *Ibid.*, p. 283.
[37] *Ibid.*, pp. 297, 364-66.
[38] Wilson and Linken, p. 119.
[39] *Ibid.*, p. 121.
[40] Donald B. Louria as cited by Wilson (ed.), *Adolescent Drug . . .* , p. 254.
[41] See "Letters to the Editor," *Science News,* 95 (Apr. 19, 1969), 374.

5. Tranquilizers

The term "tranquilizer" is not looked on with much favor today in the best pharmacological circles. Drugs which would fall under this heading are now classified differently, without the use of the offensive term. They are:

Drugs Used for Allaying Anxiety

This class would include meprobamate (Miltown).

Drugs Used for Treating Neuroses or
Functional Nervous Disease

Here there is no question of disease dependent upon an evident lesion of a body tissue. The illness to be treated is of psychic or nervous origin. Nervous tension, for example, may be present and require relief by drugs of this class.

Drugs Used for Treating Psychoses or Severe Emotional Disturbances, Including Madness or Insanity

Drugs Which Will Precipitate a Kind of Mock or Pseudo Psychosis

Lysergic acid diethylamide (LSD) and similar agents belong in this category and are known as psychotomimetics or psychotogenic drugs.

It becomes evident from this classification that a very wide variety of drugs are known today which affect the human (or animal) psyche (mind or soul). This development represents something fairly new in biological science.

ALTERNATE CLASSIFICATION

Drugs affecting the psyche can be classified in various other ways. And since classification systems throw light on the psychic and other actions of these agents, we will note just one alternative classification to the above.

Tranquilizers Used to Treat Anxiety Neuroses and Psychoses

Such a class would include Miltown, reserpine, phenothiazine derivatives, etc.

Antidepressive Drugs, or Drugs Which Act as
Psychic Energizers

These may also be known as thymoleptic agents. Such drugs would include tea, coffee, amphetamines, etc. Their effects may partially, at least, neutralize those of the tranquilizers. That is, they produce an elevation of the mood, or euphoria, rather than depression.

During the clinical trial of new drugs active against tuberculosis it was noticed that those patients who had been treated with iproniazid showed not only improvement of their tuberculous lesions but also of the depression which was a result of their disease. In fact, it was reported at the time that the normally tuberculous and lethargic patient showed high spirits. Some maintained that patients danced around the hospital wards under the influence of the tuberculostatic drug. In fact, iproniazid was much more active as a mood elevator than as a tuberculostatic agent. That is, the dose required to produce mood elevation was much less than that required to control tuberculosis. Thus, a therapeutic dose for tuberculosis proved to be a heavy overdose for mood elevation. The use of the drug for tuberculosis was therefore abandoned, and investigation commenced for its use as a mood elevator. Soon other substances, some chemically allied to iproniazid and some not, were found to possess similar mood-elevating properties.

Psychotomimetics Which Do Not Cure Psychic Disturbances But Precipitate Conditions Resembling Those of a Diseased Psyche

These drugs may precipitate symptoms in the human (or animal) resembling insanity. Drugs in this category may be subdivided as follows:

1. The true hallucinogens such as mescaline, opium, hashish *(Cannabis indica)* and marijuana *(Cannabis sativa)*. Alcohol, as taken in the later stages of chronic intoxication, may belong in this subgroup when it produces the hallucinations of delirium tremens.
2. Psychedelic drugs or drugs possessing so-called "consciousness-expanding" properties already described.

DESCRIPTION OF THE TRANQUILIZING DRUGS

Turning from classifications, we must now devote some attention to the general class of drug formerly designated as "tranquilizers" and which alleviate anxiety, neuroses and psychoses. Let us consider for a moment the drug which created so much interest ten years or more ago and which is still used widely today, especially in combination with other drugs. It is known as meprobamate or Miltown.

Meprobamate

This highly popular drug has two main pharmacological actions which result in the allaying of tension and anxiety and the supervention of a feeling of well-being.

First, meprobamate physically relaxes nervously tensed muscles. This relaxation produces a general reduction of the tensed-up feeling, making the patient feel better. Second, meprobamate sedates the central nervous system in a manner similar to that shown by barbiturates. In fact, it is fair to state that meprobamate acts like a barbiturate of low potency in many of its pharmacological properties. A very low dose of an ordinary barbiturate will often produce an effect similar to that of a relatively high dose of meprobamate.

Good advertising, coupled with the fact that meprobamate, chemically speaking, is not a barbiturate (about which physicians are rightly cautious) accounts for a good deal of its success. Moreover, it is a very nontoxic substance and does relieve tensed nerves when used appropriately. It is, however, one of the milder tranquilizers. Let us look for a moment at a much more powerful tranquilizer.

Reserpine

This substance was isolated some twenty years ago from the Indian plant known as *Rauwolfia serpentina*. The root of this plant has been used for centuries in Indian folk medicine as a remedy for insanity and other conditions.

Reserpine is an extremely active and potentially dangerous substance whose effect on the body (and mind) is highly cumulative. This means that doses build up in the body over long periods and are only very slowly excreted.

As a tranquilizer. A single intraperitoneal injection of as little as one to two milligrams per kilogram of body weight of reserpine in the mouse will tranquilize the animal for up to fourteen days. This tranquilization may be so deep that the animal goes into hypothermia (lowered temperature), becomes ataxic (loses its orientation and becomes unable to walk) and is therefore unable to feed or drink. To keep the animal alive it is necessary to inject saline and sugar solution, otherwise it wastes away to death. The major effect produced by reserpine is therefore that of sedation or strong tranquilization of the central nervous sytem in animals and men.

Lowers blood pressure. The second main effect is not so easily apparent. Because reserpine lowers the blood pressure, it is used today where tranquilization coupled with reduction of blood pressure is required. So reserpine is not only a strong tranquilizing agent, but also an antihypertensive substance.

Undesirable side effects. However, these desirable properties are not gained except at a price. Reserpine is potentially a dangerous substance since its depressant effect lasts a very long time after ingestion has ceased. The depression has often led to suicide or to attempts at suicide. Other side effects are produced as a result of reserpine's side pharmacology. A stuffy nose is a well-known symptom provoked by the use of reserpine.

A further important pharmacological side effect encountered when using reserpine is connected with its so-called catecholamine-depleting effect. Animals or men fed on small amounts of reserpine lose their supply of stored biogenic amines such as epinephrine, serotonin (5-HT) and norepinephrine. These important catecholamines are leaked away from their storage sites into the bloodstream under the influence of reserpine. In the bloodstream they are oxidized to harmless products by the agency of monoamineoxidases present in the body. If other medicaments, such as monoamine-oxidase inhibitors (MAO inhibitors), are given for mood elevation while reserpine is being administered, the catecholamines, leaked away from their storage sites under the influence of reserpine, are ro longer destroyed. As a result, their concentration builds up in the blood. Since these catecholamines are stimulants, their increasing concentration in the blood brings with it an increasing neutralization of the tranquilizing effect of the reserpine given originally. The result is that the subject is no longer tranquilized but becomes agitated and may go into seizures. Thus the tranquilizer reserpine given in the presence of an MAO inhibitor causes extreme agitation instead of tranquilization. This whole phenomenon by which the tranquilizing effect of reserpine is changed into a stimulatory effect, is known as "reserpine reversal."

A similar and potentially dangerous effect is sometimes seen in another but related drug situation. Monoamine-oxidase inhibitors are sometimes prescribed in psychic depression and are fairly common drugs. However, if blue cheese or another amine-containing food is ingested at the same time as the MAO inhibitor, the latter inhibits the metabolism (i.e., the destruction) of the stimulating amines from the cheese. The concentration of the amines then builds up progressively in the blood until the patient goes into a seizure or becomes exceedingly excited. This phenomenon has been known to be lethal in cases where very active MAO inhibitors, such as Tranylcypramine, have been used. The use of Gorgonzola or other amine-rich cheese, or other amine-containing foods can thus be dangerous during medication with MAO inhibitors. Lethal seizures can result.

Conditioned and unconditioned reflexes. The tranquilizing effect of reserpine and other similar tranquilizers is connected with their ability to suppress conditioned reflexes while leaving unconditioned reflexes practically unchanged. Thus, if an animal is given an hypnotic dose of a drug such as phenobarbital, all its reflexes—both conditioned and unconditioned—are reduced; and it will react less or not at all to both, for it is in a comatose sleep.

An animal may be conditioned to take refuge on a wooden platform when a bell is rung, so as to avoid receiving a punishing electric shock a little later. Normally the animal will run to the wooden platform the moment it hears the warning bell being rung before the shock is given. But if the same animal has been treated with reserpine or any other major tranquilizer, the ringing bell will not cause it to run to the wooden platform. That is, its conditioned reflex to bell ringing has been reduced. But, when the electric shock comes after the bell has rung, the tranquilized animal will run to the platform—though too late. That is, the tranquilizer does not suppress the animal's unconditioned reflexes.

A tranquilizer is therefore defined as a substance which suppresses conditioned reflexes but which leaves unconditioned ones substantially unchanged. Prolonged lack of sleep shows the same effect on the human. Sleeplessness will lengthen the reaction time required for conditioned reflexes, or suppress them in the same way that a major tranquilizer does. Prolonged sleeplessness renders conditioned reflex response weak, which accounts for the danger involved in driving an automobile when overtired. The human conditioned reflexes, which make up so much of driving skill, become weakened by lack of sleep; hence, the danger of driving a car while taking tranquilizers. Exhaustion from exposure and starvation can produce similar effects, as we shall see shortly.

Phenothiazines

Tranquilizers other than reserpine may achieve similar results to those attained with this ancient Indian remedy (*Rauwolfia,* reserpine). The class of substance known as the phenothiazines is in many ways similar, pharmacologically speaking, to reserpine, though some side effects may be different.

Chlorpromazine. The first tranquilizing phenothiazine discovered was chlorpromazine (known originally in France, where it was discovered, as Largactil). Chlorpromazine tranquilizes in much the same way as reserpine, but its mechanism of action is different. It does not cause leakage from the body's catecholamine stores and therefore does not produce "reserpine reversal" when given in the presence of MAO inhibitors. It is generally used as a strong tranquilizer in psychoses and in cases where simultaneous reduction of blood pressure is not required.

Chlorpromazine is more easily handled than reserpine and its effects wear off more quickly so that there is much less danger of cumulation. However, chlorpromazine belongs to the chemical class of compounds known as the phenothiazines and will, therefore, precipitate the toxic symptoms common to this class of compound. Agranulocytosis (a blood disease) is among these toxicity effects.

Will Power. Under the action of the above-mentioned type of potent tranquilizing agents (including reserpine and other sedatives), the patient becomes yielding, weak, apathetic. His will power is broken, he becomes indifferent to the world around him, and wants only to be left in peace, undisturbed. In fact, in order to avoid being bothered in his state of weakness and apathy, he will usually be ready to do things he would otherwise never do. He may even be prepared to sign false documents or to make false confessions. These well-known pharmacological effects precipitated by tranquilizers and other sedative agents have been exploited systematically by the politicians of certain countries.

TOTALITARIAN PSYCHOPHARMACOLOGY

The National Socialists

There are, of course, methods of reaching states of apathy, or tranquilization such as described above, without the use of drugs. The will can be undermined by purely physical methods such as exposure to prolonged hunger or cold, to torture or to other inconveniences involving stress. It is perhaps even safe to say that the spectacular effects of drugs on the mind tend to be overemphasized today, probably due to the novelty of psychopharmacology.

Forgotten methods. The enthusiasm resulting from the discovery of something new has brought with it the fact that the older means by which a man can be reduced to a "vegetable" by nonpharmacological means tend to be overlooked. Even though today there may be "a pill for everything," one must not forget that the expert totalitarian politician can often achieve his ends more elegantly without the expenditure of time or money on pills. A similar effect on the mind can be produced and the victim's will be bent to the will of a dictator by purely physical methods which have been in vogue as long as man has been man.

If the National Socialists in Germany wished to obtain a "confession" from their political prisoners without leaving a trace of evidence, they knew just how to destroy the prisoner's spirit swiftly and surely, leaving scarcely a mark on him and without even contaminating his food (which might have been proved by a biochemist's examination of the prisoner's blood, urine or feces).

Cold-water treatment. A favorite method (still a favorite in some countries behind the Iron Curtain) involves "the cold-water treatment" in which the prisoner is taken to a "bathroom" whose entire interior is sprayed automatically with high-pressure, ice-cold water jets every fifteen or thirty minutes. If the "treatment" takes place in winter, the windows are kept open day and night. The prisoner is taken to this bathroom, stripped of all his clothes and locked in for the night. The temperature may be anywhere between 0°and 30° F. Under these icy conditions the victim is treated all night at automatically controlled intervals with a copious and freezing shower. Needless to say, he has had little to eat or drink for several days beforehand and is weak and hungry. If he wishes to avoid pneumonia and death from exposure, he must run around his prison vigorously and continuously all night long. By morning he is suffering from extreme exhaustion and from exposure and is usually in a mood to "talk" in the way his mentors wish.

He is then "interviewed" by shifts of officials who badger him mercilessly. During the interview the interviewers will smoke, eat cookies and drink coffee nonchalantly, while the prisoner can scarcely answer a word due to weakness and exhaustion. If he falls asleep he is wakened with cold water over his whole body, or with a blow. He is informed that if he dies of pneumonia, his own doctor will verify to his wife and children that he died of natural causes (i.e., heart failure or pneumonia), so that all his "pig-headed lack of collaboration" in not signing is absolutely futile. Few indeed are the individuals who can stand this kind of treatment indefinitely. When his "confession" is signed, the prisoner is condemned.

Romans used third-degree methods. It is often forgotten that the Romans regularly used what today would be called "third degree" methods before they questioned their non-Roman suspect prisoners. The Roman officer at Jerusalem ordered the Apostle Paul to be scourged in the presence of officials before being questioned about the cause of the uproar in Jerusalem (Acts 22:24). The end desired was the "softening up" of the potentially resistant spirit of the victim, so that the Romans obtained any information necessary without reserve or difficulties. They "tranquilized" their victims by physical means, which were as effective as tranquilizing drugs in obtaining results.

Cardinal Mindszenty Case

Thus, there are plenty of means of avoiding the use of medication in breaking down a man's psyche. But, should purely physical methods fail (and sometimes human heroism and the spirit of true martyrdom are of such a quality that purely physical means do fail) then the physical treatment is combined with the tranquilizing or sedative pill (the "pharmacological" method). The two together practically never fail in breaking down even the most heroic psyche. This combination of the two available methods of breaking the will (or altering the "mood") was well demonstrated at the February 3, 1949, trial of Cardinal Mindszenty by the Communists in Hungary.

The cardinal, very outspoken and courageous in his protests against the hostile action of the Hungarian Communists toward the Roman Catholic Church there, had even gone as far as excommunicating all journalists who attacked him and the church.[1] On December 17, 1948, he had sent a letter to all bishops in the country stating:

> I have never participated in any conspiracy. I shall not give up my episcopal office. *If you should hear later that I have confessed or that I have resigned, even if it should be admitted over my own signature, consider it a consequence of human weakness. I declare such a confession a priori null and void.* [2]

From the drug point of view the sequel to Cardinal Mindszenty's arrest is instructive:

On February 3rd, 1949, the trial against Mindszenty and several of his codefendants began. From the very start it was clear that the apathetic man who was sitting in the defendant's dock was entirely different from the one who had spoken so courageously only two months before. What had happened to him after his arrest? The mystery was removed in 1951 when two of his prosecutors fled from Hungary. Both had been appointed by the state to convict him and both had had access to the minutes of the preliminary investigations. They were acquainted with the methods that had been employed in questioning the cardinal. They surrendered to the American authorities in Austria documents from which it became clear that the cardinal had first been starved in prison for 24 days. He had then been given the so-called "cold water treatment" with tablets and injections, until he was completely broken in both body and spirit, and was willing to sign any confession of guilt that was laid before him.

The cardinal was "convinced" by his captors, with the help of sedatives, that the appointment of Dr. Coloman Kiczo as his defense counsel would be a wise move. Kiczo was a Communist. His "defense" merely echoed the accusations made by the state prosecutor. Before the beginning of the trial the cardinal was visited in his cell every day by the president of the court who rehearsed with him his part in the forthcoming "trial".

Mindszenty admitted in writing to his guilt and begged the government to stop the trial. He then arose from his seat in the dock and declared that he had written the letter of confession voluntarily. Asked about the letter he had written to the bishops before his arrest and denying *a priori* the validity of any later "confession", he declared: "My true point of view is not contained in that letter which I wrote to the bishops but in the letter which I wrote to the Minister of Justice and which was read yesterday."[3]

Toward the end of 1949 the cardinal regained his memory and was placed in a villa in northern Hungary for surveillance and convalescence. He was released on October 30, 1956, from this captivity and brought by government car to Budapest in a triumphant procession at the beginning of the fall rebellion. On November 3 he addressed the nation on Radio Budapest, stressing that he was now the same as before his imprisonment. But on November 4, with the rebellion's collapse, Mindszenty was forced to take refuge in the United States Embassy in Budapest, where he lived for many years under the protection of American Marines in a room specially wired with an alarm system to warn of any attempts to kidnap him.

Embarrassment over Death

One of the difficulties accompanying the practice of psychopharmacology with the intent to break a subject's will is that of the embarrassment caused if he dies while in the hands of his tormentors. Many subterfuges are employed to avoid this difficulty. Delayed-action drugs are sometimes difficult to time correctly, but they have been used. Sometimes the "patient" has died on the aircraft taking him back from the dictator state or shortly before boarding or after leaving. The deaths of Gottwald and Zapotocky were connected in the press of certain neutral countries to delayed toxicity of this kind. The same press connected the sudden death of the Indian prime minister while negotiating a treaty with Pakistan in a third country to treatment he received there. Prime Minister Shastra was admittedly in a delicate state of health anyway and might have died from natural causes. But the neutral observers make the point that just because of this precarious state of health he unexpectedly succumbed to the psychopharmacology of his hosts.

It is significant that the late Dr. Konrad Adenauer, prime minister of Germany, when visiting a certain country known to practice psychopharmacology, neither ate nor drank anything except that which he had brought with him on his special train and which was prepared by his own cooks. Further, he consented to sleep only in his special train during the whole conference. At conferences of statesmen in Geneva, Switzerland, Russian planes fly in the totality of food from Moscow every day for the VIP Russian diplomats. They are taking no risks in the field of which they know the dangers.

This account should give us a little insight into the achievements and potential horrors of modern psychopharmacology. Both drugs and physical stress can bend the mind. But when psychopharmacology is combined with torture (physical means), as is regularly the case in many police offices in various countries of the world today, the consequences are such that whole nations can be held for ransom by a few determined political criminals.

[1] Kurt Hutten, *Iron Curtain Christians,* p. 171.
[2] *Ibid.*
[3] *Ibid.,* pp. 174-76.

6. The Amphetamines

Compounds of this class belong to the stimulatory category of substances, which, in German, are referred to by the apt name of *Weckamine*, that is, the amines which produce wakefulness or alertness. They are designated "sympathomimetic" because their use mimics stimulation of the sympathetic nervous system.

Amphetamines

The amphetamines produce vascular effects resembling those characteristic of ephedrine (isolated from the plant genus *Ephedra*) and therefore may be used as nasal decongestants. Ephedrines produce, in addition to nasal decongestion, some stimulation of the central nervous system, wakefulness, elevated mood, moderately raised blood pressure, quickened pulse rate together with raised cardiac output. There is dilation of the bronchi, pupillary dilation and inhibition of alimentary tract peristalsis. Glycogenolysis (breaking down of glycogen in the liver to liberate sugar, which passes into the bloodstream and raises blood-sugar levels) is not provoked by the ephedrines as it is by the catecholamines, such as epinephrine.

Amphetamine (Benzedrine, Dexedrine, Cydril, etc.) is a simple aromatic primary amine to which the other sympatho-mimetic amines are related chemically and pharmacologi-cally. The following scheme shows the basis of the chemical relationships:

Amphetamine (Potent CNS stimulant, appetite controller)

Methamphetamine (Desoxyn, methedrine) (Potent CNS, stimulant, appetite controller)

Phentermine (Wilpo) (CNS stimulant, appetite controller)

Epinephrine (a catecholamine, vasocon-strictor)

Norepinephrine (Catecholamine and vasocon-strictor natural hormone)

Ephedrine (bronchodilator, used in asthma)

Naphazoline (Privine) (nasal decongestant)

Xylometazoline (Otrivine) (nasal decongestant)

Serotin (5-Hydroxytryptamine, 5-HT)

(Natural hormone, function uncertain)

Catecholamines

Epinephrine, norepinephrine and serotonin are hormones naturally present in the body. Serotonin is found in platelet cells in the blood, in mast cells, in the epidermis and in the brain. Its precise function is at present uncertain as far as mammals are concerned, but it has proved to be a neural transmitter in *Venus mercenaria* (clam).

Severe mental depression follows the exhaustion of brain serotonin after treatment with reserpine such as has already been described (chap. 3). Epinephrine and norepinephrine are both released on stimulation of sympathetic nerves. Epinephrine is the principal hormone produced by the adrenal medulla, and when its concentration in the bloodstream is increased by release from the medulla during stress, the results are dilated pupils, viscid saliva, relaxed bronchi, vasoconstriction (except coronaries), sweating, tachycardia, increased cardiac output, inhibited alimentary tract peristalsis and secretion, together with relaxed bladder and ureters. These are the physiological reactions required to prepare the body to brace itself against stress. In fact, the catecholamine hormones we have been describing, together with certain corticosteroid hormones, form part of the chemical mechanism for preparing the body to meet and withstand stress.

ABUSE OF SYMPATHOMIMETIC AMINES

From this brief description of the pharmacology of the sympathomimetic amines, some reasons for their abuse in modern society become clear. The natural hormonal catecholamines, such as epinephrine and norepinephrine, are chemically and pharmacologically related to the amphetamines, so that in many ways a concentration of amphetamine in the bloodstream may behave similarly to a concentration of naturally released epinephrine during body stress. Both classes of substance produce the physiological preparation to brace the body for shock or stress. The rapid pulse rate, the increased respiration rate, the dilated pupils, the tingling in the body members, the mental alertness and clarity, the raised blood-sugar concentrations—all these physiological effects are coupled with the release of sympathomimetic amines from the renal medulla into the bloodstream under stress.

If chemically and pharmacologically related amphetamines are now introduced into the bloodstream, either by injection or by ingestion through the mouth, the body becomes prepared by them for stress in a similar way as it is prepared for stress by the natural hormones. The central nervous system is stimulated, the heart rate increases, breathing becomes more rapid and the members may tingle as vasoconstriction takes place and mental clarity and alertness result. When the mood is thus elevated to a state similar to that produced by natural stress, the subject feels a purely synthetic or artificial thrill of excitement. The taking of amphetamines or similar substances allows the user to experience the thrills and excitement of stress in a purely synthetic and artificial manner, without actual stress being involved.

ECONOMICS OF DRUG DEALING IN AMPHETAMINES

Methedrine (methamphetamine), commonly known on the street as "speed," is being used to produce this synthetic excitement in increasing amounts today. The hippies warn that "speed kills," but it is sold for ingestion, snuffing or injection at $2.00 to $2.50 per spoon (about a gram). Made in private laboratories it may cost about $30.00 per pound. A "stash" (large supply) gets broken down to half pounds, ounces and spoons. It is sold in small stationery store envelopes. A "stash" may be hidden under the stairs, in an old trunk, "fishhooked" down an empty apartment shaft or even concealed under garbage in out-of-the-way alleys.

When amphetamines are being peddled, a small taste of the compound is usually given first. Then as people get "turned on" under its influence, more and more will be demanded and sold on the spot. Some dealers can make up to $1,000 daily in tax-free profit, selling amphetamines. Some peddlers with smaller financial ambitions sell the drug merely as a means of gaining a profit, which provides them with free supplies of the drug for personal use. It is reported in some areas, though some say just the opposite, that dealers generally are shifting away from marijuana (until recently the most widely used illicit drug in the U.S.), to "speed."

Methedrine became the "rage" in the fall of 1967. It is estimated that in Boston "speed" freaks currently shoot up to three pounds a week; and the city of New York, which is reputed to be one of the biggest Eastern markets, takes thirty pounds a week.

PHARMACOLOGY OF AMPHETAMINES

Clinical Activity

The pharmacology of amphetamines and sympatho-mimetic amines in general may be conveniently classified under four main headings:

1. central nervous stimulation to produce increased alertness, mental clarity and less lethargy
2. reduction of fatigue
3. suppression of appetite
4. production of vasoconstriction, especially in engorged mucous membranes, with resultant nasal decongestion and bronchodilation

The volatile amine bases were formerly widely used under the last heading until it was realized that the first three were also important clinically. Later it was discovered that the properties under the first three headings can be fairly effectively divorced from the fourth by modifying the chemical structure of the amphetamine type of molecule to yield a new molecule possessing strong vasoconstrictor properties but weak central nervous system stimulation. Such modifications of structure have resulted in the marketing of compounds of the methylhexaneamine (Forthane) and naph-azoline (Privine) types. Compounds such as ephedrine act chiefly by vasoconstriction, with a resultant rise in blood pressure and bronchodilation, rendering them useful in the treatment of asthma.

Thus, the four main pharmacological headings given above represent a spectrum of pharmacological activity which can be split into its various components in various compounds. Some of the amines under consideration are more active in central nervous system stimulation, others excel where appetite control is concerned and again others show most activity as nasal decongestants or in relieving asthma. Phenmetrazine (Preludin) is one drug in which anorexic action (appetite-reducing action) is pronounced at the expense of the other properties associated with this type of molecule.

In general the amphetamines are rapidly absorbed from the gastrointestinal tract but are slowly metabolized and excreted. These properties make them relatively long-acting drugs. In spite of this, in order to obtain constant alertness in the face of fatigue, it is necessary to dose the amphetamines about once every four hours. To combat "morning melancholy" and other mild forms of depression, one dose immediately after breakfast (if taken before the meal, the appetite is reduced) is usually sufficient.

For the treatment of narcolepsy (uncontrollable sleep) large doses every four hours may be required and have proved to be valuable. Few organic toxic side effects have been noted, even after treating with high doses for many years. During World War II the maximal military dose of amphetamine permitted was ten milligrams in twelve hours or thirty milligrams in one week. Thirty milligrams is a teenager's average weekend dose of Benzedrine, which is reckoned to be about one-quarter of the maximal clinical dose.

Activity in Various Animals

Amphetamines are not only active in mammals and humans. A 1 percent solution of amphetamine applied to the abdomen of fireflies causes persistent glow. Spiders treated in the same way may begin to spin their web rapidly and erratically. Five-day-old chicks respond to amphetamines by continuous twittering and excitement, though some amines of this type may induce lethargy in chicks.

Activity in Various Organs

Amphetamine acts on the skeletal muscle to produce increased tone and contractility. It probably reduces muscle fatigue directly in the muscle itself and not by any action mediated via the brain. There is evidence that, in the central nervous system, amphetamine produces more rapid spinal reflexes. This effect neutralizes the slowing of reflexes resulting from barbiturate medication. In line with this action it has been confirmed that amphetamines increase the capacity for mental processes,[1] such as those involved in counting columns of figures. It is much more difficult to prove that more complicated mental processes are facilitated by amphetamines.

One of the more bizarre properties of amphetamine which has allegedly been noted by habitués is its shriveling action on the penis. "It makes your mouth dry. It shrivels your penis. It gives you hallucinations. You get the horrors if you stay blocked too long."[2]

Amphetamine Euphoria

The taking of amphetamines is accompanied by a feeling of well-being (euphoria), wakefulness and alertness, but no addiction as such occurs. That is, withdrawal symptoms are not produced on stopping amphetamine medication, and no craving for the drug occurs. Tolerance may develop, necessitating the taking of larger and larger doses in order to achieve the original effect. But if the drug is not taken for a week or two, the tolerance is lost and patient sensitivity is restored to its original level.

Activity in the Social Group and Work Increase

No antisocial behavior has been noticed that could be directly attributed to amphetamine medication. High doses of amphetamines precipitate headache, agitation, confusion, vertigo and apprehension and are often followed by mental depression. Small doses suffice to produce euphoria, so that large doses are unnecessary and undesirable. A ten-milligram dose of amphetamine may give 60 percent work improvement on a bicycle ergometer. In the two world wars soldiers and airmen have found amphetamines vital in maintaining alertness on long missions and turns of duty, where vigilance may be lifesaving. On such occasions it has been found that amphetamine itself is about ten times as effective as caffeine in reducing fatigue from muscular work.[3]

Amphetamines, Hypertension and the Blood

At therapeutic dose levels the amphetamines do not

markedly increase the blood pressure, so that they are not contraindicated in hypertension. In fact, in obese hypertensives the amphetamines may so reduce the appetite that weight loss follows, bringing with it a resultant fall in blood pressure. Cases showing a systolic blood pressure of 210 have been found to fall to around 150 in the course of time under amphetamines. However, a transient rise in blood pressure may occur where sensitivity to amphetamines is present.

Generally speaking, it is maintained that amphetamine medication leaves the blood picture unaltered, although there may be an initial contraction of the spleen which may cause a rise in the red blood cell count over a short period. The chronic use of Benzedrine over nine years in the treatment of narcolepsy showed no chronic effect on the blood picture. However, blood coagulation is hastened in some animals by amphetamine medication.[4]

The amphetamines are commonly taken to extend and intensify a weekend, to avoid the necessity of a hotel room and sleep, and thus to exploit to the maximum the free weekend time. Teenagers today do not seek the blind alcoholic intoxication of their fathers and grandfathers. They want greater awareness rather than blind drunken escape.[5] They seek mental clarity and confidence. It has often been pointed out that in this state of heightened awareness, such as that produced by the amphetamines, the sex drive is usually reduced. In this state young girls are less likely to become pregnant than they were during the drunken rowdiness following the alcohol abuse of years ago, during which the sexual drive was sharpened but awareness blunted.

Just how the amphetamines release the energy for extra awareness and alertness is not known. There are probably two mechanisms, one involving a direct effect on the intact muscle and reducing fatigue, the other involving direct central nervous system stimulation.

Toxicity and Behavioral Effects

What is generally referred to as acute and chronic toxicity

is low in the amphetamines. Using high doses, tolerance may develop and psychoses may be precipitated. However, if dosing is stopped for a week or so, the body again becomes as sensitive to amphetamines as it was originally.

Amphetamines and Diabetes Mellitus

There is, in general, little effect on blood sugar concentration attributable to amphetamine treatment. Thus, diabetes mellitus is not a contraindication for amphetamine treatment. In fact, obesity, and the maturity-onset diabetes often associated with it, often constitute an indication for amphetamines, since they reduce obesity and calorie intake by appetite control.

In general, amphetamines do not influence respiration rate in the normal person, but they do raise the respiration rate in persons suffering from morphine and other narcotic respiration rate depression.

Mechanism of the Alerting Reaction

The renewal of energy availability by amphetamine treatment takes the form of a "forced loan" on the physical reserves of the body.[6] This "lift" lasts a few hours and is always followed by exhaustion and depression. If, when the depression is setting in, the subject takes more amphetamine, he drains his physical reserves even more and enters what might be called physiological bankruptcy, which may lead to death if the process is repeated too often. The "hippies" have long since found out that "speed" kills.

Promote group instinct. One side effect of the amphetamines is that they induce psychic malleability, group sociability and group exploration. That is, the amphetamines favor the tendency of young people to act as a group, promoting the "herd instinct" or "togetherness." This may explain some action carried on by groups under the influence of amphetamines. This fact may perhaps be coupled with the observation that the toxicity of amphetamines is largely dependent on the number of animals in a cage when they are given the drug in toxicity experiments. Chance noticed that mice crowded together die from smaller doses of sympatho-mimetic amines than is the case where less crowding occurs.[7] Lasagna and McCann[8] found that the $L.D._{50}$[9] for ampheta-mine is 15 mg./Kg. $\pm$ 6 i.p. for mice in crowded cages, and that for the same strain of mice kept singly in cages the $L.D._{50}$ was 111 ± 13 mg./Kg. If, however, the crowded mice were given a large dose of phenobarbital, chlorpromazine or promazine together with the amphetamine, the toxicity of the amphetamines for the single and crowded mice became about equal. It seems that the crowding, therefore, led to the quicker exhaustion and death of the mice under the influence of amphetamine. They stimulated one another more under the influence of the amphetamine, reacting and dying in convulsions or exhaustion. The tranquilizers or barbiturates prevented this exhaustion process resulting from mutual group stimulation under the influence of amphetamines.

The same process will probably be in effect in groups of teenagers under the influence of amphetamines. They stimu-late one another in the crowded groups and bars, leading to greater amphetamine effects than if they were alone. The psychic malleability is especially noticeable in teenager groups, who become willing, under amphetamine, to "follow their leader."

Children's behavior problems. Related to this group effect is the use of amphetamines in the control of behavior problems in children. Charles Bradley and Margaret Bowen[10] showed that the amphetamines exercised a striking effect in controlling antisocial behavior in children. In introspective, withdrawn or lethargic children, amphetamines brightened up their mood and made them apparently happier and more sociable. Remarkably enough, the same treatment helped the noisy, aggressive, quarrelsome child to become quieter and less choleric. On the other hand, if true psychopathology such as schizophrenia is present, the amphetamines produce little stimulatory effect even in large doses. In fact, it is almost diagnostic of psychopathology if large doses can be tolerated without effect in children. Doses as high as sixty milligrams can be withstood in such cases, with little effect on sleep. In fact, Bradley[11] found that amphetamines were useful in certain types of aggressive child psychopaths. Such children slept very deeply, suffered from nocturnal enuresis until they were relatively mature (eleven years of age), had excessive sexual appetite and often had a history of epilepsy in the family. Amphetamine sulphate in high dose quieted such patients, in contrast to its stimulatory effect in normal children, sleep was not disturbed and emotional expression was matured, producing more harmony at home. Thus even child psychopaths treated with amphetamines showed the group effect.

In spite of the above "group effect" the connection between amphetamines and juvenile delinquency has probably been exaggerated by the news media. The police object to juveniles taking amphetamines because they say they provoke fights when juveniles are on the go all night. But, aside from this police view, the general opinion is that the chief danger of amphetamines lies in habituation (not true addiction) and in amphetamine psychosis. Ten Benzedrine tablets (fifty milligrams) are reputedly sufficient to precipitate a psychosis lasting up to a week in any normal person.

Cause of psychotogenic action. The psychotogenic action of amphetamine is thought to be due to competition by the drug for amine oxidase, which is the enzyme system used by the body for detoxifying epinephrine. Thus, under the influence of the inhibiting or competitive action of amphetamine on amine oxidase, the latter cannot destroy epinephrine, the concentration of which then builds up. Since epinephrine is an essential brain hormone and possesses a structure related to that of the hallucinogen mescaline, psychosis may set in, possibly being caused by the high concentration of epinephrine which is believed to be psychotogenic in the same way as mescaline. Further, epinephrine can be transformed into adenochrome, which some believe to be hallucinogenic too.

Amphetamines precipitate a paranoid type of psychosis with persecution delusions and auditory and visual hallucinations. The whole hallucinatory process takes place in a clear consciousness and resembles acute or chronic schizophrenia. The condition may be antidoted with barbiturates, but relapses followed by suicide often occur. To give a true picture of this rather macabre picture, it must be remembered that it is usually only the previously psychically disturbed person who takes large doses of amphetamines, so that those suffering from amphetamine psychosis are usually those suffering from psychic instability anyway. Thus, amphetamine toxicity may look worse than it really is, for those showing toxicity symptoms (psychosis) are those who would probably have become psychotic sooner or later without having taken drugs at all. An excellent description of amphetamine psychosis is given by P.H. Connell.[12] Many amphetamine habitués become afflicted with what has been described as the "cleaning up" mania. They may work for hours at arranging clothes in drawers and closets but never manage to get much in order.[13]

Even a very small dose of amphetamine will increase the hallucinations of schizophrenics. Children who are unstable due to parental rejection are particularly liable to fall prey to amphetamine habituation.[14] In fact, it is believed that amphetamine drug dependence, like all other drug dependence, is a symptom of personality disorder rather than a condition picked up from bad company and poor drug control.[15]

Phenmetrazine (Preludin) which is an amphetamine type of substance widely used in appetite control, has shown itself to be habituating, particularly in Sweden, where there has been a serious epidemic based on its abuse. A detailed report on this subject has been made by Lennart Ljungberg.[16]

Amphetamines in Enuresis in Children

One of the main functions of the cortex consists in inhibition of reflex activity.[17] In the matter of enuresis in children it is believed that insufficient cortical inhibition of reflex urination is present. In the maturation process the cortical inhibition increases and controls involuntary reflex micturition. Nocturnal enuresis is thought to merely show that, when cortical activity and inhibition are lowest, reflex micturition may take place.

If now the cerebral adaptive mechanism does not develop sufficiently at maturation, stimulation of the cortical impulses through the thalamoreticular relay by the use of amphetamines may produce the required cortical inhibition of reflex micturition (nocturnal enuresis) if the anatomical structures are intact. This cortical stimulation could develop only after about one and a half years of age, since the basic cortical activity is only mature enough after this age.

Amphetamines given to correct nocturnal enuresis have been successfully used in about 50 percent of children experimented upon. No side effects were found if low doses were used, but increases of dosage produced restlessness and insomnia. It was also noted that the general psychological state of the children at school improved under the treatment.[18] Doses of about 2.5 milligrams of amphetamine sulphate were used on retiring; these were increased up to ten to fifteen milligrams daily. If d-Amphetamine is used, the dose level in milligrams should be halved.

Other Uses of Amphetamines

Geriatrics. Amphetamines have been used with success in geriatrics, where they have been found to increase alertness and to decrease the lethargy of old age. If doses are carefully adjusted, side effects are minimal.

Postoperative lethargy. Similarly, postoperative lethargy has been successfully treated with amphetamines. It is possible in this way to release patients a few hours after tonsillectomies. The depressive aftereffects of morphine have been corrected by the same regimen. Barbital anesthesia can be interrupted, too, by amphetamine medication.

Obesity. Its use in obesity and weight-control programs by appetite reduction is so well known that description here is unnecessary, although it ought to be remarked that if obesity is of endocrine origin, amphetamine treatment is of little use. On the other hand, obesity coupled with diabetes mellitus responds well to amphetamine treatment, as does ordinary obesity in children.

Pregnancy. Some clinicians recommend amphetamines for control of undue weight in pregnancy. At the same time the depression and lassitude often associated with pregnancy are also corrected.[19] No changes were noted in either the babies born, or their mothers, after the amphetamine treatment. Ninety percent of the mothers so treated gained relief from morning sickness, whereas only 13 percent of the expectant mothers taking ascorbic acid as placebo gained any relief from nausea. One cannot, however, be overcautious about treating pregnant women with any kind of medication, knowing that pregnancy is accompanied by an extreme sensitivity to medication of any kind. The fetus and neonate are particularly likely to suffer from drug toxicity. What the long-term results may be on a fetus in later life no one can guess until long-term experiments have been carried out. This is especially difficult to do in view of the fact that the average adult usually does not know to what drugs he was exposed in utero by his mother or what he was given as a baby and in early childhood. Until comparatively recently, little research had been done on the relationship between medication in utero or later in the neonate, and the incidence of adult diseases. The catastrophe of a few years ago, which produced thousands of limbless and otherwise deformed children as a result of in utero medication with Thalido-mide—used for the treatment of quite mild disturbances in pregnant women—has precipitated a furious wave of research on just this problem. The relationship between in utero exposure of the fetus to drugs, and the catastrophe of deformed limbs or limblessness has been proved. Obviously, other less drastic relationships may exist between exposure of the fetus or neonate to medication and later disease. For the younger an organism is, the more it is likely to respond to drugs either pharmacologically or from the point of view of toxicity.

The use of amphetamines in pregnant women and young children cannot be compared, of course, to the Thalidomide catastrophe. But in view of the known extrasensitivities in early life, one cannot be too careful in using any drug in pregnancy or early life, no matter how apparently innocuous the drug may be, and this includes amphetamine.

For pep or thrills. It is clear that the true medical use of amphetamines should be sharply distinguished from the indiscriminate use of these substances to obtain "pep" or thrills. Such use constitutes abuse both to the individual taking the drug and to society.

The veterinary use of amphetamines to "pep up" race horses and other animals—headline news for some time now—is well known. The mechanism of action is the same in animals as in man.

Chronic use. Finally, although amphetamines are not truly addictive in the sense that heroin and morphine are addictive and produce craving and gross physical dependence, yet tolerance and habituation to all amphetamines can and do arise with chronic use. That is, an individual may become psychologically dependent on or habituated to these drugs and, in order to maintain a constant effect, may require larger and larger doses as a result of rising tolerance. On withdrawing amphetamines in such cases, no withdrawal symptoms arise which might be comparable to those arising on withdrawing heroin.

Where addiction to narcotic drugs like heroin has occurred, amphetamines are often peddled among such addicts in order to antagonize narcotic drug depression. Thus, amphetamines are often found in the haunts of "hard drug" addicts.[20]

Other Sources of Kicks and Hallucination.

A summary of the effects of airplane glue and gasoline

sniffing has been compiled in Charles E. Tart's book.[21] These practices are widespread today and are not without danger.

[1]Chauncey D. Leake, *The Amphetamines,* p. 39.
[2]C.W.M. Wilson, "The Patterns of Drug Abuse," *Adolescent Drug Dependence,* p. 400.
[3]Leake, pp. 42-43.
[4]*Ibid.,* p. 47.
[5]Peter Laurie, *Drugs,* p. 73.
[6]*Ibid.,* p. 72.
[7]Leake, p. 59.
[8]*Ibid.,* p. 60.
[9]The dose required to kill 50 percent of the experimental animals in a given period of time.
[10]Charles Bradley and Margaret Bowen, "Amphetamine (Benzedrine) Therapy of Children's Behavior Disorders," *American Journal of Orthopsychiatry,* 11 (1941), 92-103.
[11]Leake, p. 89.
[12]P. H. Connell, *Amphetamine Psychosis.*
[13]Nils Bejorot, "An Epidemic of Phenmetrazine Dependence," *Adolescent Drug . . . ,* p. 63.
[14]Laurie, p. 77.
[15]*Ibid.,* p. 78.
[16]See Lennart Ljungberg, "The Control and Treatment of Phenmetrazine Dependence in Sweden," *Adolescent Drug . . . ,* p. 335 ff. Also see pp. 424, 444, 458.
[17]Leake, p. 84.
[18]*Ibid.,* p. 87.
[19]*Ibid.,* p. 104.
[20]For further literature on amphetamines see the following standard reviews: G. Bonhoff and H. Lewrenz, *Ueber Weckamine* (Pervitin and Benzedrin),(Berlin: Springer, 1954); W.R. Wett, L.H. Howells, and A.D. MacDonald, *Amphetamine in Clinical Medicine: Actions and Uses.* (Edinburgh: Livingstone, 1955), pp. 17-35; A. Wikler, "The Relation of Psychiatry to Pharmacology," *Amer. Soc. Pharmacol. Exper. Therap., (Baltimore: Williams & Wilkins, 1957).*
[21]Charles E. Tart, (ed.), *Altered States of Consciousness,* pp. 363-475.

7. The Morphine Drugs

USE OF TERMS

It has become increasingly difficult to handle the question of habituation to the so-called "soft" and "hard" drugs under the old nomenclature using the term "addiction." It has been resolved, therefore, to substitute for the terms "addiction" and drug "habituation" the term "drug dependence." The WHO Expert Committee on Addiction Drugs (1964) endorsed the following definition: "Drug dependence is a state of psychic or physical dependence, or both, on a drug, arising in a person following administration of that drug on a periodic or continuous basis. The characteristics of such a state will vary with the agent involved, and these characteristics must always be made clear by designating the particular type of drug dependence in each specific case; for example, drug dependence of morphine type, of barbiturate type, of amphetamine type, etc."[1]

Some experts are of the opinion that "the myth that there is a definite difference between hard drugs and soft drugs should be exploded. It is not only misleading but, frankly, incorrect.... Many people talk about morphine and cocaine as being hard drugs and marijuana as a soft drug, therefore it is not possible to differentiate between soft and hard drugs on a legal basis (because marijuana is classed legally with morphine and cocaine). They cannot be differentiated on a pharmacological basis because morphine is a drug which produces physical and psychic dependence; in consequence it is classified as a hard drug. On the other hand, cocaine produces only psychic dependence; barbiturates which are often classified as soft drugs, produce both physical and psychic dependence in exactly the same way as does morphine. People with experience in this field claim that the physical dependence produced by barbiturates, is, in fact, more severe, and the withdrawal syndrome is more serious than that occurring with morphine. Again, amphetamines produce marked psychosis. On this basis amphetamine is probably far more of a dangerous drug to the individual's psyche than is heroin. Therefore any definition which tries to differentiate between hard and soft drugs should be abolished. This point is now generally accepted."[2] Even drugs such as aspirin can produce a kind of dependence.[3]

USE BY ADOLESCENTS

Drug-abuse experts usually give the following reasons for adolescents starting drugs: (1) the desire for new experience; (2) curiosity about perception; (3) to improve oneself; (4) religious philosophical needs; (5) to increase self-knowledge.

Many practical-minded observers of the present drug epidemic do not connect it with complex causes in modern society but relate it simply to the boredom of modern suburbia. Idle hands will always find mischief of some sort. "I think that boredom is one of the central points in the increase in the crime wave. Drug addiction is connected with this."[4] "In the United States, we ought to accept that we are a drug oriented, kicks oriented society. We have too much leisure time, and will have more in the future. This is just as true in Europe as it is in the U.S."[5] There is no denying the common sense of this summing up of the problem for the mass of adolescents tied up in suburbia with nothing really challenging to do.

OPIUM

One of the most common and most injurious drugs of addiction is opium. Opium is a mixture of many substances, and pure narcotics such as morphine may be isolated directly from it. Acetylation of morphine results in heroin which is one of the most powerful analgesics and addicting agents known.

Opium is found in the poppy *Papaver somniferum* which has been cultivated for supplies of opium for many centuries, especially in the Orient. The crude opium may be either smoked or eaten. When eaten, the poppy capsules are crushed and mixed with water to form a drink known in the Orient as *Kasumba, Post* or *Kuknar*. The crushed mixture may also be taken in the form of a pill twice or three times a day. For centuries China was the country in which large amounts of opium in one form or another were consumed.

Opium also was (and is) used for doping or sedating infants and for relieving pains and spasms. Arabian medicine was well acquainted with the properties of opium and used it as an anesthetic and analgesic. Arabians prescribed it for relieving pains in the head, eyes, teeth and joints. It was also used for drying up catarrh, and allaying coughs, asthma and hiccups. Maniac delirium and inflammatory conditions of the brain were also treated with opium, as were epilepsy, facial paralysis and other nervous conditions. Some Arabian physicians used opium for treating spermatorrhea and also as an aphrodisiac.

The Tibbi (Mohammedan) *materia medica* lists the following opium preparations:[6]

1. *Barshasha*—used for catarrhal conditions of mucous membrane, cough, epilepsy, diarrhea and premature seminal discharge

2. *Hib-i-pecheash*—for use in the treatment of dysentery
3. *Hubi-i-jadwar*—used as for Barshasha
4. *Hub-i-siyah*—used for conjunctivitis and ocular pain
5. *Hub-i-sarfa*—used as cough mixture
6. *Hub-i-haiza*—used for treatment of cholera
7. *Kurs-i-massalas*—used topically for headache and other pains
8. *Hub-i-mumsik*—used as an aphrodisiac pill against premature seminal discharge

In the East, as already mentioned, opium was given regularly to children to keep them quiet while their mothers were working. It caused a general predisposition to ill health, ulcers and constipation. Conjunctivitis was often present in such children and most were grossly underweight, though potbellied. Children who had regularly received opium in this way were readily weaned from the opium habit as soon as they became more independent of their parents for feeding. In this their opium addiction differed from that of adults.

The drug has also been used as a general stimulant after the age of forty-five to fifty years to help overcome the fatigue of manual labor. Pills containing doses of between one-half grain and four grains were swallowed for this purpose. In China, opium is generally smoked but in India it was (and is) usually ingested. These paradoxical effects of opium, that is, the stimulatory and the sedative effects, are fairly typical of addictive substances in general. Addiction can be produced, in fact, by mixing a sedative such as a barbiturate with a stimulant such as an amphetamine and ingesting the mixture at one time.

Symptoms of Opium Indulgence

The first symptoms of opium smoking in the novice are those of euphoria. Aches and pains disappear and a feeling of elation supervenes. Delightful, languid pleasure follows, and the smoker feels at ease with and superior to his fellows. Afterward, if the smoker falls asleep, pleasant and vivid dreams occur. With continued smoking over a period of time the smoker often becomes apathetic, lazy and unkempt. But, after the first new pipeful, he becomes talkative, exaggerative, self-confident and considers himself to be logical and intelligent. He smartens up his outward appearance, polishing his shoes and combing his hair. He loses his sense of time. Social distinctions between the smokers (generally opium smoking is a social affair) disappear, and the ritual of preparing to smoke is carried through with great pleasure. Tea and sweet food are usually served to all present. There is no hurry but only leisurely enjoyment of the preparations for the delights of smoking, even though the surroundings are those of the dirtiest, darkest opium den.

With the progress of the habit the smoker experiences great changes which may even end in dementia. He loses weight, becomes pale and more and more subject to all kinds of diseases. His appetite disappears. The drug craving grows but the euphoria during smoking becomes less and less marked. At this stage the main effect of smoking is to lessen the deep depression in which the smoker now habitually finds himself. He feels just a little more normal and less depressed after a smoke. If smoking is denied the opium addict, withdrawal symptoms set in which include great prostration, vertigo, torpor, watery discharge from the eyes, acute distress and cramps together with insomnia. A single pipe of opium will alleviate all these symptoms temporarily. Heroin and morphine addicts show similar withdrawal symptoms since the same basic drugs are involved.[7]

The Opium Habit and Crime

In India, at least, the popular idea that the opium habit is always associated with crime is not completely true. In that country a good percentage at least of apparently normal individuals have over the years indulged moderately in opium without catastrophic effects. Such users employ the drug to tide them over difficult periods of their lives or to help them to combat pain.

The effects of opium smoking are more accentuated than

those of opium eating since the drug is more surely and quickly absorbed through the lungs into the general circulation. Smokers are often of sallow, muddy complexion, with sunken eyes and cheeks. In addition they are often anemic. Their eyes look dull and sleepy, their tongues are coated, their breath foul and they give the impression of suffering from chronic intestinal toxemia. Subcutaneous fat may be reduced and the muscular tissue below wasted. Dry throat is common, and the respiration rate is below normal and shallow. On the other hand some addicts can remain apparently normal if they obtain their "fix" regularly. Violent crimes are rarely committed by the ordinary moderate user of opium, but maladjusted persons rapidly become heavily addicted and they may then resort to crime to satisfy their craving for the drug. One sees here again the fact that it is not always the drug itself which is dangerous, so much as the combination of the drug plus the maladjusted person.

Cure of Opium Smoking

It is more difficult to cure opium smoking than to cure the opium-eating habit. Therefore attempts have been made to cure opium smoking by allowing the smoker only to eat the drug. Smoking gives a much more powerful and intense drug effect than that produced by merely eating the opium, so it is difficult to persuade the smoker to turn back to the less intense pleasure of merely eating. The treatment of opium smoking has not been developed much in the West since opium smoking is not a widespread problem here.

The habit of opium eating, although less dangerous than opium smoking, is far more difficult to throw off than alcoholism.

> The torments of a drunkard deprived of his accustomed stimulus, described so graphically by Charles Lamb, are as nothing to the sufferings of the devotee of opium, when striving to release himself. "His sufferings," says Openheim, "when deprived of the stimulant, are as dreadful as his bliss is complete when he has taken it. Night brings the torments of hell; day, the bliss of paradise!" . . . And the English

opium-eater compares his sufferings, when attempting to break off the vice, an attempt in which at last he succeeded, to the tortures of the rack.[8]

HEROIN, CODEINE AND MORPHINE

Heroin—often known as "horse"—codeine and morphine are derivatives of opium, and addiction to them represents one of the most disastrous problems afflicting modern civilized society. Codeine is the least addicting. Addiction to heroin and morphine is such a massive problem and the literature on it is so voluminous that only the briefest summary is possible within the framework of this book.

Addiction Given up Voluntarily

Although addiction to the so-called "hard drugs" (the opiates) is a very serious matter and should not be minimized in any way, yet it is often forgotten that many addicts do give up their addiction voluntarily when they reach thirty or forty years of age. The most dangerous years for addiction are those immediately following adolescence. This process of voluntarily giving up drug habits is often referred to as "maturing out."[9] There is a heavy concentration of addiction between the years of twenty and thirty. Few become addicted today after fifty years of age.[10] There is little difference in the addiction rate between the sexes. Young rats are more easily addicted to morphine than older animals.[11]

Proportionately to the general population there are more physician opiate addicts than nonmedical addicts. This arises from the fact that the physician (or the nurse) knows the properties of morphine better than the nonmedical person and may take it to relieve an alcoholic hangover or to steady his nerves when under stress. Michael J. Pescor has given an excellent description of the physician addict.[12]

Statistics on Addicts

The Federal Bureau of Narcotics asserts that there are nearly 60,000 heroin addicts in the United States, but Dr. Efren Ramirez maintains that there are 100,000 heroin addicts in New York alone. New York City Police Commissioner Howard Leary maintains that 10 percent of all persons arrested in New York City admit to being users of narcotics.[13] Addicts commit at least 20 percent of all the burglaries which take place in New York, amounting to $1 billion in goods annually. Dr. Marie Nyswander holds that heroin addiction is an ever growing problem among adolescents although it has declined somewhat among Negroes in the past decade. Others maintain that opiate addiction is a relatively small problem in the United States.[14]

Need of the Addict

The driving need of the drug addict is such that he will go to any lengths to obtain a "fix." Morphine itself, and its crude source—opium—are highly addictive, but heroin, the diacetyl derivative of morphine, is even more so. As a painkiller, heroin is more powerful than the mother substance, morphine, and is also, in a parallel manner, more addicting. The drug may be taken by sniffing, hypodermic syringe, smoking or by mouth.

Why do some individuals develop the urge to take drugs while others do not? Some experts believe that there is a predisposition to addiction.[15] But most individuals addicted to drugs are considered to be self-centered and narcissistic. They seem to be interested only in the satisfaction of their own primitive needs.[16] Some maintain that experimentation with heroin in youngsters usually follows a period during which reefers were smoked; others doubt this very much.[17]

Example of Dangerous Effect

To illustrate the dangerous effect that heroin and morphine may have on abusers, one example will suffice. A professor had just finished lecturing to his pharmacology class at noon and dismissed his students. One of his "A" students was returning to his university dormitory for lunch. As he was passing through the swinging doors he saw a fellow from his dormitory also leaving the building. The student greeted him in a friendly way with "Good morning," whereupon the young man turned on him in a fury, shouting that the student had insulted his race and was mocking him.

The student stood aghast as the young man then whipped a knife out of his pocket and plunged it several times right through the student's chest—so deeply that the point appeared through his back. Then the young man made off, leaving his victim lying in his own blood. He managed to crawl, in spite of extreme loss of blood, to a children's clinic a few yards away. It took fourteen pints of blood to save his life. The knife had missed his lungs and his heart by a fraction of an inch.

The student's attacker had been employed in the university hospital and had been discovered stealing narcotics, for which he had been dismissed. Thus his source of narcotics had dried up on him and he woke up with the driving need of a "fix," which he could not obtain. Being thus "on edge" from his craving for narcotics (probably morphine in this case), he was in the mood to attack anyone without the slightest real provocation. This is one of the great problems in our highly organized civilization—the dangerous drug addict let loose on society which knows nothing of its danger.

The saying goes "Once a junkie, always a junkie." There is a great deal of truth in the saying, for treatment of the addict is extremely difficult and has not progressed much in recent years. We must therefore look shortly into two aspects of the heroin, morphine and opium addiction problem. How is the addict produced? How is he treated?

THE MAKING OF THE MORPHINE, HEROIN OR OPIUM ADDICT

It is said that in New York City at least one person in eighty is addicted and that one addict can bring about the addiction of four or five new individuals yearly.[18] This may be exaggerated.

Three Necessary Factors

To produce an addict to any drug three factors are

supposedly necessary: an emotionally disturbed person, an available drug, and a "pusher" or other mechanism by which the two are brought together. The affluent and competitive society has provided plenty of emotionally disturbed persons as well as the means to buy expensive drugs of addiction. It has been noticed that boys brought up in a matriarchal society are especially prone to drug addiction. The lucrativeness of the drug trade together with the driving need of the addict to obtain his "fix" at any cost does the rest. "Pushers" will always be found if the profit offered is sufficiently high. The person who has become addicted then aggravates the situation still further by acting as a missionary and inciting others to get "hooked" too. Certain and quick relief from the tensions of modern life is a tempting bait to offer to some disturbed younger or older person of the affluent society today, particularly those who have been overprotected during college and family life and who are now for the first time on their own.

Blame Drug Laws

Over and above these causes of addiction some others must be taken into account in explaining the addict. Some physicians who have studied drug addiction carefully, are of the opinion that the United States drug laws contribute heavily to encouraging addiction and its misery. Dr. Marie Nyswander believes that "the artificial American tragedy with real victims" began with the enactment of the 1914 Harrison Act. Before this act the most widespread cause of narcotic addiction in the United States was undoubtedly the inclusion of narcotics in patent medicine. Dr. Nyswander writes,

> Before the addictive power of opium and other drugs was recognized, at least a million people in this country were exposed to addiction through patent medicines and physicians' prescriptions. Because of the soothing and analgesic properties of opium and its derivatives, these drugs were used indiscriminately to relieve everything from headache to angina pectoris. Various remedies with a narcotic

content of 5 to 10 percent were sold without restraint over the counters of pharmacies all over the country. Through such wonder-working medicaments as Mrs. Winslow's Soothing Syrup, Dr. Cole's Catarrh Cure and Perkins' Diarrhea Mixture, incredible amounts of opium, morphine, codeine and cocaine were spooned into children as well as adults. Every well-equipped home had a rosewood chest, counterpart of the present day medicine cabinet, with its ball of opium and its bottle of paregoric.[19]

Even heroin, one of the most addictive narcotics extant, was used for twelve years without its addictive properties being recognized. As late as 1913, doctors in the United States were free to treat addicts as they thought fit and the addict could buy morphine over the counter.

Addict Turned to Underworld

The Harrison Act put an end to all this. But it was administered by law-enforcement officials and not by physicians. Treatment of addicts by physicians was forbidden and many physicians were thrown into prison for treating their addict patients. The result was that the addict could no longer turn to his physician for help in his craving and need, but had either to turn to the underworld for a supply of his drug or to the law-enforcement officer. When the legislators and enforcement officers ignored the shocking physiological needs of the addict in his addiction, he turned to the underworld to obtain the only relief known to him—the illicit "fix."

After the famous Behrman case, in which the United States obtained a verdict against Dr. Behrman for giving an addict large quantities of morphine, cocaine and heroin for self-administration, the Federal Bureau of Narcotics began what has been called "a reign of terror" by Rufus King, a lawyer particularly interested in the narcotics problem. Any prescribing of narcotic drugs by physicians to put an addict on an even keel was forbidden, so that the "addict patient" disappeared and the "addict criminal" emerged.[20]

Surprisingly, when Dr. Charles O. Linder was charged with

having sold an addict informer one tablet of morphine and three tablets of cocaine for self-administration, the Supreme Court unanimously vindicated the physician for his action. But in spite of these cases supporting the right of the physician to treat the addict-patient, by 1925 the pattern had been set, in which the physician refused to treat the addict with the drug he needed.

> A Physician who treats and/or prescribes drugs for an addict-patient in good faith according to medical standards will be protected from conviction. But his good faith (and here lies the catch) and adherence to medical standards can only be determined *after a trial*. The issue of whether the doctor acted in good faith and adhered to proper medical standards must be decided by a judge or a jury. If the judge or the jury decide against the physician, the latter may be sent to prison or deprived of his license to practice medicine.[21]

Thus, as Judge Ploscowe points out, the physician has no way of knowing before he attempts the treatment of an addict whether after a trial by jury he will be vindicated, or condemned to prison and his license to practice medicine revoked. The only safe courses open to the physician are to refuse to see the addict, or to see that he is handed over to some official detoxification center to have his addiction "cured."

Limit Physicians and Hospitals

The consequence of this state of affairs is that, in general, medical schools and physicians have been cut off from contact with narcotic addiction, which again leads to their having little practical experience with it. Thus the administration of the Harrison Act has resulted in the private physician having little to do with the addict who may seek his help. Neither can the normal hospital find physicians to treat addicts who ask for their help—for no physician is going to risk the penalty of prison or the loss of his livelihood. Hospitals, too, have enough ordinary patients and do not want to be filled with addicts who may introduce bribery and corruption to persuade auxiliaries to provide them with "fixes." This would again introduce trouble with the legislative authorities and render the hospital liable to prosecution under the Harrison Act.

Thus the lawmakers have practically closed the American clinic and hospital to the addict and intimidated the American physician, as well as taking from him his undeniable right to treat addicts as he sees fit in the interests of good medical practice. The result is that only the Federal Bureau of Narcotics can do anything at all. This bureau has the right and monopoly to try out its theories on curbing and treating addiction. These theories are perfectly simple, but unfortunately they have been shown by the history of law in many countries to be entirely futile. For they are based on the belief that more and harsher measures will intimidate people away from drugs.

"Narcotic Prohibition"

Increasingly severe and unreasonable measures are proposed as the means of controlling drug addiction. Even the death penalty has been proposed for certain offenses involving minors. I have known of two students thrown into prison without hearing and incommunicado for four days for picking a week growing on the roadside which turned out to be hemp! Surely every student of history and human nature knows that severity and severity alone will never cure any problem of this sort.

There are many who believe that very strict control of the sale and availability of narcotic drugs would control addiction. "If no drugs were available, no one could be addicted to them" is the thesis. It is a very tempting approach, being so obviously simple and logical. But it is true only to a certain degree. A look at the attempt to control alcoholism by Prohibition ought to be sufficient to reveal the weaknesses of the approach. It is the human factor which nullifies the logic of this method. It is obvious that if drugs are cheaply available to all, the drug problem will be aggravated, so that strict control is indicated in whatever plan one adopts. But as long as man and society are what they are and open to the temptation of both profit and doing something against the law of the Establishment, "Narcotic Prohibition" is going to succeed to about the same degree as Prohibition itself did. Strict control of drugs will keep the average law-abiding citizen away from them, just as Prohibition did with respect of alcohol among the same class of people. But there is a certain "sink" of addiction which will never be controlled by punitive or legislative measures of any kind. In fact, if punitive measures drive the profit of the "pushers" up, they may increase illicit traffic.

Thus, it seems likely that by carefully controlling availability by means of regulating laws, one can reduce addiction to a certain minimum. But any and all displacements of this equilibrium may be likely to increase addiction. It follows that police control and legislation of the punitive sort will never be able to eradicate addiction, which means that it will always be necessary to treat the addict medically, as a sick person.

Many believe that it was the punitive approach which was instrumental in closing the narcotic clinics which were opened in the United States after World War I in an attempt to stop the spread of addiction. These clinics were intended to treat the addict as a sick person and not as a criminal. That is, they were supposed to work on the so-called "British System" which allows the physician to treat an addict with the minimum dose of the drug to which he is addicted with the aim of keeping the addict "normal" and comfortable so that he can work and lead a normal life. These narcotic clinics were closed prematurely without having had a real chance to show their value.

THE NATURE OF OPIATE ADDICTION

Most addict patients consider the drug to which they are addicted as the cause of all their ills and at the same time the source of their only pleasure. Hence, the term "G.O.M." (God's Own Medicine) for narcotics on the one hand and the terms "junk" and "crap" on the other. Injection of the drug is equivalent to partaking of both good and evil, with perhaps special emphasis on the latter.

"Alimentary Orgasm"

Rado developed the idea that opiates allow the addict to achieve an intestinal, as opposed to a genital, experience which he called an "alimentary orgasm."[22] He considered that this alimentary orgasm was to be equated with sexual immaturity of the oral type, which again was to be compared with the bliss of an infant receiving warm milk at its mother's breast.

Narcotic drug experience viewed in this light is obviously both compelling and convenient. For it is an easy, convenient substitute for the more valid but complicated interpersonal sex relationship. The drug method of obtaining satisfaction is much easier—it is simply injected in a matter of seconds just where and when the addict wishes. This sexual implication brings some people to consider the "cure" of addiction to opiates as about as unlikely as it would be to hope to "cure" a man of sexual intercourse.

Guilt Feelings

If narcotic drug injection does, in fact, produce an "intestinal orgasm" it is not surprising to find guilt feelings associated with each narcotic injection, just as guilt is often associated with masturbation or illicit sexual relationships.

The addict will regularly vow that this present injection which he is in the process of carrying out will be positively his last one. Over and above these specific guilt feelings there have been numerous reports of incestuous feelings being associated with the shooting of narcotics.[23] This probably arises from the fact that many addicts have had dominant mothers and have lived in matriarchal families and societies in which the male is dependent on and subservient to the female. Thus there may be, in addicts of this type, an unnatural relationship between man and woman, and the child often has (subconsciously) toyed with incestuous attitudes toward its mother. Following this line we find addicts asking forgiveness of their mothers (mentally, at least) just before and during the shooting of a narcotic. Thus addiction may be connected with perverted sexual attitudes.

Where mixtures of cocaine and heroin are used—often considered to be the acme of addiction—the addict often has a feeling of having "blown up the world" in his act. After this act he may feel that he has been left without personality and is completely numb.

When the orgastic feeling which follows injection is over, the addict sinks into a feeling of oblivion. He "goes on the nod" or starts "coasting." After this stage is over, grandiose feelings of power and fantasy come, during which all problems seem to be of easy solution and in which personal problems can be faced as never before. As this drug effect wears off, the same old problems rise again in their old strength just as they were before the last shot.

As the time for the next shot approaches, the addict will remember that he almost achieved complete euphoria the "last time," but not quite. This coming shot will, then, in his mind, bring complete euphoria and, having achieved that, he will shoot no more. This is how the repetition compulsion arises.

Loss of Potency

In line with the above characterization of opiate injection as being comparable with an "intestinal orgasm," we find that, as we would expect, such substitute intestinal orgasm brings with it loss of sexual libido and sexual potency. However, even while under narcotics there may still be a desire on the part of male addicts for associations with the opposite sex. But such relationships are usually perverted, for in them the male addict is usually totally dependent on the woman. Aggressiveness, so characteristic of the normal male, is also reduced under narcotic addiction. Heroin or morphine will tame the most aggressive psychopaths and make them cowardly idlers—with the possible exception of the aggressiveness or cunning displayed by addicts during withdrawal when they need to obtain a "fix" at any cost and by any means. But, in general, narcotics make addicts docile, impotent and yielding. In fact, they psychologically castrate or emasculate the male for a time, in the same way that a sexual orgasm does.

From the above we may conclude that opiate addiction seems to be in some ways a type of substitute sexual experience in which "intestinal orgasm" replaces the genital one. Indeed, intestinal orgasm renders the addict for a time incapable of the normal sexual orgasm, addiction allowing the narcotic addict to "achieve a libidinal goal" with orgastic pleasure. "Such a phantasmagoria of psychic effects can, in fact, be observed in greater or lesser degree in many young addicts." [24] Rado has said, "Erotic gratification by means of drugs is a violent attack on our biological sexual organization." [25]

TREATMENT OF HEROIN AND MORPHINE ADDICTION

If the morphine or heroin addict does not receive his "fix" he will experience withdrawal symptoms which can be, in severe cases, excruciating. They consist of nausea, cramps and chills commonly known as "cold turkey." One "fix" will remove all these symptoms quite quickly, so quickly, in fact, that the British describe an addict as a drug-dependent person who is normal when dosed with the appropriate dose of the drug to which he is addicted.

Addiction Easily Detected

Today it is relatively easy to detect addiction to opiates. One can even determine fairly accurately to how much opiate an addict is addicted. That is, one can form an idea of the doses he has been taking by the following method: The suspect is treated with a graded series of doses of Nalline (nalorphine), a competitive antagonist of morphine. If after dosing with Nalline the suspect shows morphine withdrawal symptoms, he is an addict. The Nalline deprives the body of the morphine or other opiate effect on which the addict is dependent. This it does by competing for the receptor sites at which the opiate is effective. Since the morphine or other opiate has been displaced by the Nalline, the addict is physiologically deprived of his opiate drug and will experience "cold turkey." The dose of Nalline he needs to precipitate "cold turkey" gives an idea of how great his addiction to morphine derivatives is. This method of detecting addiction is used in California and elsewhere, and is employed before treatment in some cases.

Dr. Leary's View of Curing Addicts

Dr. Timothy Leary takes a rather unusual view of curing opiate addicts. He writes:

> It is of interest that the heroin addict and the illuminated Buddha end up at the same place. The void. The junkie is a deeply religious person. The alcoholic is, too. Thus our physicians and psychiatrists have no luck in "curing" addicts. If you see an addict as a social misfit, a civic nuisance who must be rehabilitated, you completely miss the point. To cure the junkie and the alcoholic, you must humbly admit that he is a more deeply spiritual person than you, and you accept the cosmic validity of his search to transcend the same, and you help him see that blackout drugs are just bad methodology because you just can't keep holding the "off" switch, and that the way to reach the void is through psychedelic rather than anesthetic experience.[26]

In other words, Dr. Leary's view is that the junkie should leave narcotics (opiates) alone and seek the void in psychedelic drugs. The end of both types of drugs is the same, but narcotic (opiate) abuse is just bad methodology.

At the drug-addiction center in Lexington, Kentucky, it has been found that there is a 96 percent relapse rate for patients (addicts) who voluntarily underwent treatment there but for varying reasons discharged themselves prematurely.

Methadone

One method of treating heroin and morphine addiction involves the use of another analgesic drug, a synthetic known as methadone. It is often used to replace morphine as an analgesic, is long-acting and itself somewhat addictive. It produces less sedation, less smooth muscle spasm and less respiratory depression than morphine, also less miosis. After becoming addicted to methadone, withdrawal symptoms are minimal. In addition to these properties methadone possesses the ability of blocking the euphoric action of the opiates. As long as a heroin addict remains on methadone he cannot be readdicted to heroin or similar opiates. Dr. Nyswander reports that of 383 heroin addicts taken into her program (with Dr. Vincent P. Dole) only 33 were dropped or left the program on their own.[27] They maintain that the rest, many for the first time in their lives since addiction, became self-supporting, responsible citizens.

Methadone is not the final answer to opiate addiction since the addict has to take it permanently to achieve his freedom from morphine and its derivatives.

"Normal" Treatment of Opiate Addiction

Admittance to institution. In the United States normal treatment begins with the admittance of the volunteer or prisoner to the institution. In other countries, where the addict may be treated as a normal sick person, methods may be different. The first work to be done is to search the prisoner or volunteer thoroughly for concealed drugs, syringes or needles. The seams of clothing, false heels of shoes, packages hidden in the hair under the armpits, tubes concealed in the mouth, all these subterfuges are common. In women, the vagina has to be thoroughly searched, for entire hypodermic outfits have been found there. Similarly, the rectum must be searched.

The patient is then *physically* examined. If tuberculosis or myocarditis are present the treatment may have to be modified. Tuberculosis is very common in addicts who have been on drugs eight to ten years or more.

If the patient is strong enough, some authorities prefer to withdraw the addicting drug at once. Others withdraw them gradually. Heart attacks followed by death are quite common during sudden withdrawal from prisoners who have been using high doses of narcotics and who are debilitated.

Usual patient reaction. During treatment the narcotic addict is generally docile unless he is in withdrawal. The withdrawal period is particularly dangerous during addiction treatment because not only is the discomfort of "cold turkey" intense then, but the temptation to obtain a "fix" is accentuated since most addicts know that euphoria is greater if narcotics are shot at this time. He will generally submit to the treatment prescribed for him. To obtain his "fix" he will display considerable cunning, nerve and acting ability. But once he has the drug in his possession he is likely to be completely naïve. He will hide the drug, for example, in the same pant's cuff he had hidden it in when he was arrested the last time. But, aside from his cunning, the narcotic addict longs to be told what to do and will do it, even to going to the hospital for treatment. However, when he finds the hospital and its treatment not to his liking, he will discharge himself and blame the person who advised him to undergo the treatment. He wants to put all blame and responsibility on other people.

The City Prison, Manhattan, has observed and treated in recent years more than 16,000 addicts per annum and has noted the greatest percentage increase in addiction during the year 1966.[28] Habit formation is definitely on the increase. Less than 2 percent, according to the Manhattan figures, owe their addiction to physicians' prescriptions. It is generally a case of friends having introduced them to "snow" or "happy dust" with the addictive consequences.

Factors determining treatment. Once inside the institution, the treatment of the patient or prisoner will depend on the following considerations: (1) his physical condition, (2) the length of the period for which he has been addicted, (3) the daily dose and type of narcotic he has been taking, (4) his reasons for taking the drug (maladjustment, depression, social history, etc.), and (5) whether he has been addicted to other drugs (e.g., barbiturates) as well as the present narcotic.

It is the opinion of many specialists in this area that, although depressant drugs may be used during the excruciating phases of narcotic withdrawal, their continuous administration is to be deplored. If the addict has used the narcotic for a long time and is in a debilitated condition, he must be strengthened before withdrawal is attempted. Some hospitals practice catharsis during withdrawal, which certainly does not strengthen and build up the addict for his withdrawal ordeal. In one month one hospital lost by collapse and death sixteen of its addicts who were undergoing withdrawal of narcotics. They had practiced catharsis and the administration of depressant drugs.[29]

The addict who has been addicted for only a short time is more easily cured than the chronic addict of many years' standing. If the patient is suffering from severe pain of any sort, morphine may be required to treat the pain. Under such circumstances withdrawal should not be attempted unless other less addicting analgesics are effective. Cocaine habitués may be treated by total withdrawal of the cocaine at once, since they show few withdrawal symptoms. Cocaine is one of the most toxic of the commonly used drugs. Its chronic use rapidly leads to deterioration in the addict. Some physicians have tried to replace cocaine with methyl amphetamine and find that the latter can substitute for the former at least for a time. The addicts who thus substitute become dependent on the intravenous methyl amphetamine. Under certain conditions cocaine is an aphrodisiac.[30]

Where high doses of heroin or morphine are involved some physicians prefer to withdraw the drug gradually to avoid the risk of cardiac failure under the stress of sudden withdrawal. During withdrawal the patient must be under continual observation and all medication carried out by experienced personnel. To leave a patient by himself and tell him to gradually reduce his dose (with which he has been supplied personally beforehand) is as useless as giving a drunkard a gallon of whiskey and telling him to take a spoonful less each day.

No quick treatment. There is no treatment known today which will cure an opiate addict in two weeks or even two months. The only safe way known (and even that is fraught with dangers and a high-failure rate) is to separate the addict from his old friends and surroundings, place him in a group that hates addiction (preferably a group that was once addicted) and, under the strictest institutional care, withdraw the drug from him—by a process feared by all addicts, and feared often beyond measure. After withdrawal the patient must be sent immediately from his home city to a farm or other institution where he will be well fed and made to work hard out of doors. This treatment should be carried out for at least a year. Even after such treatment, if the patient returns to his old surroundings and way of life he is liable to relapse into renewed addiction at any time. This method is considered by many conservative experts in the field to be the only really sound one. But even when carried out conscientiously the relapse rate is still high.[31]

The British System of Narcotic Drug Control

Legally the British system of handling addiction is similar to the American system. Addiction under both systems is not classed as a crime, but illegal possession of drugs is. In British territories physicians may not give an addict drugs to merely gratify his addiction. But the British Dangerous Drug Act of 1920 does allow a physician to prescribe a minimal dose of narcotic to a patient if it has been shown that the patient is incapable of living a normal and useful life without the aid of the drug. The formal proof of the addictive necessity is not demanded legally and is purposely vague. The onus of proof lies with the physician and his medical integrity.

By this legal and medical subterfuge, the British addict is kept out of mischief, the illicit drug market is undermined, the government keeps track of addicts, and the physician receives a government subsidy for writing narcotic prescriptions.

Officially there are few opiate addicts in Great Britain. Some 360 were officially known in the entire British Isles according to recent figures. In view of this situation many Americans have wished to introduce the British system in the hope that addiction would be reduced thereby in America. But many physicians and legislators fear that addiction in the United States would rise sharply if such a step were taken. For the low addiction rate in the British Isles is thought by many to be due to the fact that Britain has a sociologically more stable culture than the United States. Only some 0.2 percent of the population of the British Isles is (or was in 1950) of non-Caucasian stock, compared with 16 percent in the United States. The significance of this fact becomes apparent when one realizes that two-thirds of all addicts in the States are recruited from the latter stock.[32] In Hong Kong, which is a British Crown Colony, there was in 1957 under the British system of narcotic drug control, an addiction rate some twenty-two times higher than the corresponding United States rate. This would bear out the thesis that the low British addiction rate is not due to the British system of narcotic drug control but rather to a sociologically more stable population.

THE PHARMACOLOGICAL TYPES OF DRUGS CAUSING ADDICTION SIMILAR TO THAT CAUSED BY MORPHINE AND HEROIN

The classes of drugs which will cause addiction are the following potent pain relievers:
1. the morphine group, including morphine itself, heroin, Dilaudid, codeine and, of course, opium
2. the morphinan group (Racemorphan, Levophan)
3. the meperidine group (Demerol, Nisentil)

4. the methadone group (methadone, Isomethadone)

5. the dithienylbutenylamine group[33]

All of these drugs are addictive pain relievers and may be used by addicts. They all induce drowsiness; lessen anxiety; inhibit sexual drive (as do all opiates); cause respiratory depression, vomiting and constipation; and alleviate hunger. As with all opiates, sexual drive may be vastly increased pathologically during withdrawal, bringing with it the usual consequences. It is also typical of opiates, including morphine and heroin, that they both stimulate and depress the central nervous system at the same time. Indeed, it is this very property which is one of the marks of the addictive drug. Even phenobarbital possesses a slightly stimulating effect along with its main depressive action, which fact explains its addicting properties.

In the opiate type of molecule in general and the morphine molecule in particular, the stimulant and depressant properties lie in one molecular structure. But if one takes two different molecular structures, for example, one stimulant (such as an amphetamine) and one depressant (such as phenobarbital) and mixes the two together, an addictive mixture is formed which is the basis of "goof balls." The stimulation and the depression introduced at the same time to the body help produce the addicting effect.

Painkillers of the opiate kind cited above do not elevate the threshold for pain perception of "quick pain" but seem rather to change the total reaction of the whole organism to a painful experience. It has been shown[34] that decreased anxiety, associated with anticipation of pain, plays a vital role in opiate analgesia.

TOLERANCE

Tolerance to opiates is frequently referred to as an essential attribute of addiction. As time passes, a progressively increased dose is required to achieve the same desired pharmacological effect. However, an important aspect of this phenomenon is that tolerance does not develop to all aspects of opiate action. It develops toward the toxic, sedative and analgesic effects of the opiates, and progressively larger doses are needed to achieve the same end effect from the point of view of toxicity, sedation and analgesia. But tolerance develops only to a partial extent with respect to miosis and gastrointestinal effects. Some addicts have been known to inject intravenously up to five grams of morphine within sixteen hours without serious toxic effect. But the phenomenon of tolerance can be very dangerous. For the addict concludes that he can tolerate a really large dose—he may have injected three grams intravenously before without serious trouble. But if, for some reason, he may have been unable to shoot the large dose for a time, his tolerance may change, or he may suffer from a liver dysfunction, thus decreasing his tolerance. When he eventually obtains his large "fix" he injects the large dose he believes he needs for relief and to satisfy his craving, with the result that it kills him. Unknown to himself, his tolerance had been reduced in the meantime.

CONCLUSION AND SUMMARY

The cure of the opiate addict is fraught with difficulties. First, the primary step to cure must come from within the addict himself. He must be willing to give the drug up and must adopt a new attitude of mind toward his addiction. No one can be cured against his will, so to achieve cure the addict must be serious and willing to undergo the torture of withdrawal. Then he must be willing to be sent to entirely new surroundings, associating with a new group of people who hate addiction, although they were perhaps once addicted in the same way. This helps to give the addict a new attitude to himself and to life.

The book *Narcotic Addiction,* cited in the footnotes, gives an excellent account of the present-day theory and practice of the treatment of addiction and describes the operation of several narcotic clinics.[35] It also contains an extensive bibliography on many aspects of narcotic addiction.

Finally, some experts such as Dr. Alfred Lindesmith believe that it is correct to say, not that the addict craves drugs because he likes their effects, but that he likes the drug effects because he craves the drug.[36] For example, a large initial dose of heroin or morphine may precipitate nausea and dizziness, which normally speaking, are undesirable side effects. But the addict enjoys just such side effects because he knows that they are the accompaniment of large doses and potent drug injections.

It is a mistake to imagine that experienced addicts shoot opiates for pleasure. Marijuana gives more pleasure, generally speaking, than opiates; but marijuana is not addicting, so the pleasure aspect alone is not critical. Some experts believe the experienced opiate addict does not inject for euphoria, but merely for the relief he obtains from the pain of withdrawal. This craving for the relief of withdrawal pain is believed to be a main factor in addiction. That euphoria itself cannot be the abiding aim in addiction is shown by the fact that in late chronic addiction, little, if any, euphoria is experienced, but only a feeling of "normalcy." This theory is borne out by the fact that withdrawal of cocaine does not produce withdrawal symptoms of the opiate type. From this we would expect that ordinary opiate addiction would not be produced by cocaine, which is, in fact, the case.[37]

Thus, addiction to stimulants such as cocaine would be expected, on the basis of this theory, to be different from addiction to opiates, because the latter produce clearly definable withdrawal symptoms and the former show few of these effects on withdrawal. Dr. Lindesmith sums up the situation by saying that the "euphoria which opiates initially produce is the bait on the hook rather than the hook itself."[38]

---

[1] R. W. Rasor, "Narcotic Addiction in Young People in the U.S.A.," and P.H. Connell, "Clinical Aspects of Amphetamine Dependence," in C.W.M. Wilson (ed.), *Adolescent Drug Dependence,* pp. 21, 43.

[2] *Ibid.,* pp. 243-44.

[3] Arnold Linken, "The Psycho-Social Aspects of Student Drug Taking," *ibid.,* p. 166.

[4] *Ibid.,* p. 275.

[5] *Ibid.,* p. 287.

[6] *Drug Addiction with Special Reference to India,* p. 185.

[7] For further details of opium smoking see *ibid.,* pp. 190-211.

[8] John A. O'Donnell, John C. Ball and Harris Isbell (eds.), *Narcotic Addiction,* p. 50.

[9] R.E. Lister, "Narcotic Drugs in Adolescence," *Adolescent Drug . . . ,* p. 6.

[10] Rasor, p. 11, and Dean F. Markham, "Epidemiological Aspects of Adolescent Drug Dependence in the United States," p. 188, in *ibid.*

[11] Hannah Steinberg *et al.,* "Animal Behaviour Studies and Some Possible Implications for Man," *ibid.,* p. 36.

[12] Michael J. Pescor, "Physician Drug Addicts," in *ibid.,* pp. 164-67.

[13] Nat Hentoff, *A Doctor Among the Addicts,* p. 7.

[14] O'Donnell, *et al.,* p. 63.

[15] Rasor, p. 17.

[16] *Ibid.,* p. 18.

[17] *Ibid.,* pp. 19, 25.

[18] Margaret O. Hyde (ed.), *Mind Drugs,* p. 86.

[19] Marie Nyswander, *The Drug Addict as a Patient,* as cited by Hentoff, p. 30.

[20] Hentoff, p. 33.

[21] Judge Morris Ploscowe, *Interim and Final Reports of the Joint Committee of the American Bar Association and the American Medical Association on Narcotic Drugs,* as cited by *ibid.,* p. 34.

[22] Cf. O'Donnell *et al.,* p. 85.

[23] *Ibid.,* p. 86.

[24] *Ibid.,* p. 89.

[25] *Ibid.*

[26] Timothy Leary, *The Politics of Ecstasy,* p. 43.

[27] Hentoff, p. 8.

[28] O'Donnell, *et al.,* p. 23.

[29] *Ibid.,* p. 32.

[30] Lister, p. 8. *Adolescent Drug Dependence* is an excellent and authoritative account of many aspects of amphetamine and other drug dependence. This book is so important in our field of study that it is pertinent to mention here that it contains chapters on narcotic drugs, stimulant agents, hallucinogens, the pharmacology of dependence, the epidemiology of dependence, the relationship of dependence to adolescence, and regulations controlling drugs of dependence in various countries of the world. This book represents the proceedings of the Society for the Study of Addiction at a symposium held in London on Sept. 1 and 2, 1966, and is copyrighted by the society.

[31] O'Donnell, *et al.,* p. 33.

[32] *Ibid.,* pp. 206-7.

[33] *Ibid.,* p. 67.

[34] H.E. Hill, C.H. Kornetsky, C.H. Flanary and A. Wikler, "Studies on Anxiety Associated with Anticipation of Pain," American Medical Association, *Arch. Neurol. Psychiat.,* 67 (1952), 612-19. See also O'Donnell *et al.,* p. 68.

[35] O'Donnell, *et al.,* pp. 180-209.

[36] *Ibid.,* p. 97.

[37] Alfred R. Lindesmith, in *ibid.,* p. 102.

[38] *Ibid.,* p. 103.

Part Two
The Environment Factor

Introduction

IS THE TERM "MIND" CONGRUENT WITH THE TERM "BRAIN"?

We have been investigating the pure pharmacology and psychopharmacology of selected psychopharmacologically active drugs. Their effects on the body in general and on the mind in particular have been discussed in some detail.

If, now, the term "mind" were covered completely by the term "brain," that is, if the mind were a mere appendage of the brain and entirely dependent on it for its total existence, then our problem would be relatively simple. For if, in killing the brain by cutting off its supply of nutrient blood and oxygen, we at the same time wipe the mind entirely out of existence, then the mind merely a shadow of the physiological brain and disappears when the latter disappears, just as my shadow disappears when my body is destroyed.

If this is the case we could maintain that the two terms "mind" and "brain" are congruent. And if this proposition is correct and complete, then neuropharmacologically active drugs will modify the mind by merely modifying a part of our material bodies, namely, the brain. This would mean that drugs, in modifying the mood and mind, would also be modifying such things as religious faith.

Does Religion Result from Chemical Reactions?

Dr. Timothy Leary goes a long way toward confirming the fears of some that religion is a matter of chemical reactions, for he writes:

> The laboratory equipment for experimental theology, for internal science, is of course made of the stuff of consciousness itself, made of the same material as the data to be studied. The instruments of systematic religion are chemicals. Drugs, Dope. If you are serious about your religion, if you really wish to commit yourself to the spiritual quest, you must learn how to use psychochemicals. Drugs are the religion of the twenty-first century. Pursuing the religious life today without using psychedelic drugs is like studying astronomy with the naked eye because that's how they did it in the first century, A.D., and besides, telescopes are unnatural.[1]

There are difficulties in the way of such a theory. If the proposition were true it should be possible to locate in the brain the various functions of the mind regularly and easily. But surgical ablation experiments (destroying or removing various areas of the brain to ascertain which part of the "personality" is injured thereby) have given equivocal results. Efforts have been made to remove specific parts of the brain to identify the structures in which drug hallucinations are located. But even the most exact neurosurgical studies have only served to confirm in the animal what has long been known to be true for man, namely, that the effects of a cerebral lesion or ablation depend less on the site or extent of the lesion than on the previous psyche of the individual concerned and the prior treatment he has undergone, or the current treatment he is undergoing.

The same is true for monkeys, which normally show large differences of individuality and, therefore, large differences in the effects of cerebral lesions. Moreover, monkeys which have been subjected to neurosurgery often show changes in behavior and personality many months after the operative technique has been performed. Even in rats the effect of neurosurgery is very dependent on the animal's handling.[2] Evidently behaviorial changes and alterations in the psyche can occur spontaneously (pathologically), or as a result of surgery (sometimes many months afterward), or as a result of hallucinogenic treatment with drugs.

Results of Research

The result of this research has been that the relation of specific parts of the psyche (or mind) to specific parts of the anatomical physiological brain has not been very well elucidated to date. It is by no means proved that the existence of man's mind is entirely dependent on the coexistence of the brain, for correlations between the destruction of parts of the brain and destruction of parts of the mind are not so easy to demonstrate. Lobotomy experiments are known to influence personality tardily.

FACTORS GOVERNING THE MOOD

Biochemical Reactions

It is clear that mood-elevating drugs produce a stimulating effect on the mind and mood. It is evident that depressant drugs depress the functioning of the mind. Alcohol will make "the heart merry" and a good dinner will improve the mood by raising the blood sugar and other nutritional levels. As a result some educated Christians tend to regard as somewhat shocking the concept that a man's thoughts, mood and outlook are controlled by his biochemistry rather than simply by his faith. Whether he is grouchy, sleepy, tearful, hilarious, angry or raving mad; whether he is easygoing, good-natured, easy to get along with, or stubborn, is, according to some views, merely dependent on his biochemistry, his genes and how his digestion works. Correct the biochemistry and his faith may correct itself—that is the attitude of some.

There is some justification for this view. But if it were the whole truth, then faith as such and its effects on a man's life are for the birds—or biochemistry. Materialism, not faith in God, would be the answer to questions of the psyche, if biochemistry and physiology explained the mind totally. We must keep firmly in mind the fact that drugs can be used to brainwash and destroy will power and drastically modify the human personality. They can vastly modify the memory or block it, calm the neurotic, the anxious or the psychotic. One can understand how the believer in God and in the spiritual side of man may become fearful lest his faith turn out to be merely covert materialistic biochemistry. His longing for eternity and for freedom from guilt may be an illusion produced by a drug or by an amino acid in his bloodstream— or by indigestion. In fact, many materialists believe this sort of thing already and say so. Accordingly, they think religious faith really falls under the heading of a kind of materialistic pharmacology.

Sights and Sound

But there are many pharmacological reasons, in spite of or because of what we have said, to show that the psyche is not entirely materialistically bound in all its reactions and being. It is simply untrue to maintain that mood is *entirely* controlled by drugs, genes, feasting or fasting. For instance, the sight of a beautiful sunset, happy, healthy children at play, a view of the glowing Matterhorn, a happy, fulfilled old human face or the sight of the ocean during a high wind can elevate my mood considerably. Yet this elevation has not been *caused* by materially changing the contents of my blood as far as I am aware. Nor is the tranquility and joy which come to me from listening to Bach or Mozart dependent on my raising my blood alcohol and sugar by feasting and drinking as I listen. The sight of the treasures of the Wallace Collection in London or the Wyeth Collection in Philadelphia does me good, and improves my mood, even when I am hungry (to some extent at least!). So there must obviously be other factors involved in controlling and deciding man's mood or psyche than mere factors of blood content and biochemistry.

Biblical View

Sees materialistic side. The Christian revelation throws light on this problem. It maintains with all clarity that the mood is modified effectively by drugs such as alcohol, for it reports in many places that wine makes glad the heart of man and that feasting and drinking lead to merrymaking.[3] The biblical writers show no embarrassment about teaching these materialistic views on the nature of the human psyche. Such ingenuous confessions to materialistic psychopharmacology ought to disarm the materialist who is suspicious of all the Bible teaches. For here, at least, the Bible is perfectly correct in its materialism.

The Bible does not stop here, however, even though the materialist might prefer it to. For it commands the devout to "rejoice in the Lord"[4] rather than to feast and drink wine so as to be able to rejoice. The Bible commands us also, with equal authority, to "weep with those that weep"[5] (without starving).

Teaches two causes. This means that the Spirit of God, who is the self-confessed Author of the Book, teaches *that mood elevation or depression can result from two causes.* In the first case, mood changes can result from purely material causes such as blood sugar or alcohol levels, the raising of which occurs during dining and drinking. Reduction of these levels will occur during starvation and will produce the corresponding depression of mood, such as the lethargy demonstrated by the starving inmates of concentration camps. On the other hand, raising of the mood can also occur in obeying the commands of God's Spirit, or seeing a field of spring flowers, just as lowering can occur (as in the case of weeping with those that weep) by the same obedience (or by disregarding one's own conscience). In short, something entirely supramaterial, such as obeying the Spirit of God (or searing one's own conscience) can raise or lower the mood. Something which has nothing to do with biochemistry, as far as we can see, can produce a psychical effect.

The psalmist implies something similar when he exults that "in thy presence is fulness of joy."[6] This fits in, though weakly, with most people's experience of pleasure in being with friends they love. There is little that is overtly biochemical about this (unless the cause be sexual in some cases). The writer of Ecclesiastes, too, declares unequivocally that *"God giveth* to a man . . . knowledge, and joy."[7] The physician St. Luke related *joy* to being filled with the Holy Ghost,[8] which would certainly be classified by most informed people as a suprabiochemical experience. The psalmist and the Apostle Paul were also of one mind in conceiving of certain joy as a direct gift of God to his children.[9]

The Bible never suggests that this kind of joy is caused by material considerations, but implies that it is purely a spiritual phenomenon and is the reward of all those who practice God's will.[10] The Apostle Paul emphasizes just this point in his Colossian letter: "That you may be filled with the knowledge of his will in all spiritual wisdom and understanding to lead a life worthy of the Lord, fully pleasing to him, bearing fruit in every good work and increasing in the knowledge of God. *May you be strengthened with all power,* according to his glorious might, for *all endurance and patience with joy,* giving thanks to the Father."[11] Endurance with patience is not naturally thought of as the best method of becoming endowed with an elevated mood! But here endurance in doing the will of God is rewarded with God's joy. That is, joy of this type originates in God and not in blood sugars. Such mystical joy could fill a man even in the reduced biochemical condition of starvation or in mortal agony, as the record of the martyrs well proves. That is, it is here a question of a purely supramaterial gift to the mood or mind of man.

We may, then, safely conclude that the Bible knows all about both the material and supramaterial origins of mood elevation. It reports, in a quite ingenuous manner, the joy of feasting and drinking and even promises something analogous in the kingdom of God. But it teaches perfectly plainly that material sources of joy are not the sole ones available to mankind. For joy can also be a gift of God in an entirely esthetic, nonmaterial manner, especially to those who practice his will. This means that man is certainly subject to the material pharmacology of blood sugars and catecholamines. But he is also subject to other influences such as the Spirit of God—or even the beauty of the creation around him, which is an entirely esthetic matter.

Man is a hybrid being. From all this we deduce that man must therefore be a hybrid being consisting of both material and spiritual constituents. For his well-being can be influenced by material matters, such as blood sugars, and also by esthetic matters, such as sunsets, poems, radiant faces—and by practicing the will of God. Material pharmacology, such as that shown by LSD under some circumstances, can take care of one kind of joy. But there is little evidence that psychoactive drugs can cause the other kind of joy, which comes from the practice, for example, of the divine will, even though they may increase esthetic perception and cause ecstasy.

Man, being a hybrid, needs both sources of joy to remain in balance. Animal or material joys do not continually and completely satisfy him. Neither do esthetic joys always and completely satisfy him, as when he is starving or in pain; though, of course, by a special dispensation of the goodness of God, the martyr may experience a special dispensation of joy even *in extremis.* But this is not normal.

It is clear that the joy and experiences of one part of the hybrid may spill over into the other part—as when God's joy radiates into the physical face of the pain-wracked martyr, and supra-natural strength enables him to endure purely physical pain. There are no watertight compartments.

THE PHYSICAL AND PSYCHICAL CONSTRUCTION OF MAN

Examine Man's Makeup

Having presented in Part I the pure, observed pharmacology of drugs, we must now proceed to look further into the psychical and spiritual makeup of man. For a drug may influence the whole hybrid, not merely one material side of it. Just as spiritual or esthetic joys spill over to influence the body and make the physical face radiant, so a satisfied stomach can rejoice the mind by spilling over. One portion of the hybrid is inextricably bound up with the other. The material and psychical makeup of man must obviously both be thoroughly taken into account in any attempt to interpret the significance of man's use of drugs. Thus attempts at interpreting the current drug epidemic must evaluate man's hybrid makeup, otherwise a lopsided view will emerge.

Broad Analysis

For these reasons a broad analysis, rather than an analysis in depth, of man's psychical makeup is attempted in the following pages. The analysis will include as many aspects of man's attributes as can feasibly be used to throw light on the effects of drugs on the human body and psyche. Thus, we attempt to look into such questions as ESP, mediumship, dream thought, and the meaning of REM (paradoxical sleep), the nature of thought itself, the eliminative functions of the nervous system and H. Bergson's and C.D. Broad's interpretation of these phenomena, as well as the question of the survival of the human psyche after death, when it is, presumably, beyond the reach of psychopharmacology!

The orthodox pharmacologist may well take strong exception to the attempt to treat such a wide range of subjects in a book describing the action of LSD and other drugs on the central nervous system. Yet, if man is a true hybrid of matter and spirit (or psyche), it will be at once obvious that his spiritual side as well as his physical side must be treated in any valid analysis of drug action in his species. For, if we make no attempt to understand man and his hybrid physical and spiritual makeup, how will we be able to understand the effect of drugs, hallucinatory and other, on this hybrid structure? Both material drugs as well as psychical influences modify man's body and spirit. Presumably, to a less extent similar considerations apply to higher animals. Each factor spills over into the other segment of human and animal structure. Both constituents of our hybrid nature are involved in mood and its elevation, as well as in depression; in joy as well as in mourning.

Our analysis of the psychical research carried out by Dr. C.D. Broad of Cambridge, England, will show that there is good evidence for the psychical survival of the human in his out-of-the-body experience as well as post-mortem. The work reported on mediums will tend in the same direction and throws more light on the structure of man's psyche.

CONCLUSION

Finally, if man is a hybrid of material and psychical factors then we may well ask ourselves if the hybrid can ever be resolved into its constituent parts. Let us be quite clear that, although the scriptural evidence, as we see it, of man's hybrid structure leads us to believe in a trichotomy (body, soul and spirit) rather than a dichotomy as the basis of man's structure, yet it does teach equally clearly and emphatically that only the sharpest "sword" can "separate" soul from spirit.[12] Such separations lie outside the capacity of our sensory system.

Thought Without Physical Brain

There is, nevertheless, evidence that, although the physical brain is necessary for the ordinary thought processes of our hybrid organism, thought itself may exist without the mediation of the physical brain as a substrate. How else can we interpret the Chaffin case (see p. 180)? After Chaffin had died, his ostensible "shade" appeared several times to his son in the night and finally explained to him where his will was to be found. These post-mortem appearances, long after the body had decomposed, must have been concerned with post-mortem thought, that is, with thought without the mediation of the physiological brain.

The same logic applies to our Lord's thought when he went down to the realms of the "shades" and in their "prison" preached to them. [13] At the time his own body lay dead in the tomb awaiting the resurrection morning. But he preached to these spirits in bondage, thereby using thought processes (for one cannot preach or communicate without thought of some sort) without the aid of his body. The spirits in prison had long been dead, yet they must have employed thought processes in listening to and understanding the Lord. They did this without the mediation of their long since decomposed physical brains. The same kind of logic applies to all Christians who have died. For they rest in his presence and are consciously comforted, even though some of them cry, "How long?" [14] The very fact of conversation with God implies thought processes, but without the aid of their martyred material bodies. May it not be that the cases of the out-of-the-body experiences which we will discuss (see p. 181) also imply thought without the mediation of the brain, which often lay "unconscious" during the experience?

Mathematical Thought

After thinking these matters over, it becomes manifest nonsense for us to maintain that the material, physiological brain we possess is the sole source of thought processes and conceptual work in our universe. For even such nonreligious scientists as Sir James Jeans believed that the ultimate reality behind the universe was pure mathematical thought. And there is much evidence for the correctness of Sir James' views! If we were, now, to employ materialist views to the effect that pure thought is an obligate appendage of the physiological brain, just as my shadow is an "appendage" of my body, then the ultimate pure mathematical thought behind the universe must also be lodged in some kind of a superbrain out somewhere in the skies and must be supplied with a liberal supply of millions of gallons of well-oxygenated blood and biochemical nutrients in solution to keep it going! Or alternatively, it functions as a supercomputer and owns a superpowerhouse, somewhere beyond the limits of our astronomical vision, to keep it in business!

Brain as a Relay Station

May it, then, be that the brain is a relay station for thought, rather than a generator of thought? Aldous Huxley and others believed that the brain seems to be tenuously connected by some sort of valve with Mind-at-Large. Obviously such a connection could be disturbed by brain pathology (or brain maturity or senility) just as my connection with Switzerland by long-distance telephone can be disturbed without any disturbance having taken place in the thought or mind of the person whom I am phoning.

The following pages are an attempt to give the evidence for the hybrid nature of man. If we are hybrids, consisting of both matter and psyche, we must obviously take this into account, especially in dealing with drugs that influence the body and mind. In dealing with psychic factors we must realize that they may well spill over into somatic factors, precipitating physical as well as psychical disease. The converse holds too. Only the total picture, as nearly as we can arrive at it, is going to give us a reliable view of drug effects on the complete hybrid. For to understand the complexity of human (or even animal) response to psychoactive drugs demands research on the broadest basis into man's total physical and psychical structure. And even then, this foundation will be neither wide enough nor sufficiently profound to meet the challenge of increasing knowledge.

[1] Timothy Leary, *The Politics of Ecstasy,* p. 44.
[2] Leonard A. Cohen, "Drug-Induced Hallucinations," *Drugs and Sensory Functions,* Andrew Herxheimer (ed.), p. 275.

[3]II Sam. 13:28; Esther 1:10; Ps. 104:15; Prov. 31:6; Eccles. 9:7; 10:19; Matt. 26:29; Mark 14:25; John 15:1; Luke 12:19; 15:23-24; 22:18; I Kings 4:20.

[4]Phil. 3:1.

[5]Rom. 12:15.

[6]Ps. 16:11.

[7]Eccles. 2:26.

[8]Acts 13:52.

[9]Rom. 15:13.

[10]Rom. 15:32.

[11]Col. 1:9-12 (RSV).

[12]Heb. 4:12.

[13]I Peter 3:19.

[14]Rev. 6:9-10.

8. The Human Mind and Mind-at-Large

THOUGHT AS REALITY

Imposed Order

Sir James Jeans regarded the cosmos and ultimate reality not primarily as a cosmos and reality of matter, materials, elements and compounds, but as cosmos and reality of *imposed order* on and in these elements and compounds and therefore primarily of pure thought. He conceived of thought as the ultimate behind the order of matter itself. For, if we accept his view, is not matter order *ex nihilo?* And are not order and thought relatives? And is not matter a kind of crystalline (ordered) energy? Thus the meaning behind things lies in the ultimate pure thought behind them, so that the pure thought we cannot see would be at least as real as the matter we perceive. Matter is a mere outward expression of otherwise hidden ultimate thought.

Pure Thought as Mathematical Thought

Over and above this, Sir James was of the persuasion that

the reality, the pure thought, which is behind things and matter, was mathematical thought. He expressed himself on this point as follows:

> If the universe is a universe of thought, then its creation must have been an act of thought. . . .
>
> The universe begins to look more like a great thought than like a great machine. Mind no longer appears as an accidental intruder into the realm of matter; we are beginning to suspect that we ought rather to hail it as the creator and governor of the realm of matter. . . . We discover that the universe shows evidence of a designing or controlling power that has something in common with our own individual minds . . . [with] . . . the tendency to think in the way which, for want of a better word, we describe as mathematical . . . we are not so much strangers or intruders in the universe as we at first thought.[1]

Sir James was, to judge from his writings, by no means a convinced Christian. He did believe in a Mind, perhaps a Mind-at-Large, behind the cosmos, though this ultimate mind or reality behind things was, for Sir James, not necessarily Jesus Christ or the God of the Bible. On the other hand, Sir James' views were certainly more than pantheistic. He apparently never thought that the cosmos *was* God, or that the cosmos created itself and so was in itself creative. And he was certainly not an atheist. With many physicists today he believed that matter is an expression of a thoughtful or conceptual force exogenous to matter, but pervading it.

Huxley's Views

Somewhat similar viewpoints on Mind-at-Large turn up in the writings of Aldous Huxley, who, again, was not by any means a convinced Christian. In his *Doors of Perception* Huxley develops the ideas of Henry Bergson, Samuel Alexander and C. D. Broad of Cambridge to the effect that memory and sense perception, as functions of the brain, are mainly *eliminative* and not *productive* functions.[2] Huxley cites Broad as follows:

We should do well to consider much more seriously than we have been hitherto inclined to do the type of theory which Bergson put forward in connection with memory and sense perception ... the function of the brain and nervous system and sense organs is in the main *eliminative* and not productive [creative]. Each person is at each moment capable of remembering all that has ever happened to him and of perceiving everything that is happening everywhere in the universe. The function of the brain and nervous system is to protect us from being overwhelmed and confused by this mass of largely useless and irrelevant knowledge, by shutting out most of what we should otherwise perceive or remember at any moment, and leaving only that very small and special selection which is likely to be practically useful.[3]

In other words, it is potentially possible for man to perceive at any one time the whole universe and everything happening in it, as well as everything that has ever happened to him as an individual. This mass of knowledge would be useless, and indeed a hindrance to our survival, as well as an overwhelming distraction, if it were always present and continually perceived by us. Therefore, this massive flood of perception has to be stemmed if we are to be in a position to use our perceptive faculties as aids to survival.

Perhaps a related idea was intended to be conveyed to us by Solomon, reputedly the wisest man who ever lived, when he informed us that eternity (infinity, including infinity of perception) had been placed in man's heart, but that this eternity is so placed there that man cannot fathom either the end or the beginning of things.[4] Man has a perception of eternity in his heart, yet man's consciousness is not flooded by it at all!

Adam's Communion

With his Creator. A similar concept is inherent in the Genesis account of the communion which the original, unfallen Adam had with his Creator.[5] The first man, Adam, communed with God (Mind-at-Large) and, therefore, potentially with everything—with all events that ever took place or were taking place in the universe, as well as with everything that had ever happened to him. For not only had our first father's body, soul and spirit been created by God; God had also created everything that ever happened to Adam. In telling us that Adam knew God the Scripture is informing us that the finite and temporal Adam was in communion with the infinite and eternal. There was open communion and two-way perception between Mind-at-Large in eternity and man in time. Yet Adam was apparently not flooded by this perceptive width, and was able, indeed, to survive, although in a paradise of God.

With material nature. The width of perception Adam enjoyed must have extended not only in the direction of what we, in our present ignorance, call "the Beyond" (i.e., in the direction of things divine and supranatural). Adam's perceptive width included all of material nature too. For without any apparent difficulty Adam was able to catalog the earthly creatures God brought to him for that purpose—a truly formidable task for anyone under any circumstances. It seems likely, therefore, that Adam, before his fall, was capable of perceiving everything that was happening everywhere in the universe, for he was in constant communion with his Creator, besides possessing a comprehensive perception of all nature around him. Adam must have been a perceptive giant compared to modern man with his limited consciousness.

Loss Through the Fall

With the infinite. Unfortunately this huge open perceptive ability for the infinite, as well as for the finite, did not last for Adam. For, with the fall, Adam lost much of his perceptive capacity for God, that is, for the infinite and eternal. In fact, after the fall, Adam is reported to have directly hidden himself from God's presence. That is, he cut himself off from the perception of God's person, the infinite. His progeny have habitually emulated him in this and other matters ever since. Thus, with the fall, Adam's perception of the infinite became limited. He still had eternity in his heart, but it was throttled.

With nature. In addition to this perceptive loss, Adam began to suffer a second kind of perceptive loss in his view of nature herself. For she became his enemy, and he her enemy, against whom he had to struggle in the sweat of his brow to make a living. With an enemy one does not maintain the open lines of communication which one may have with a friend. The net result of Adam's fall was, therefore, the constriction of the lines of perception toward God (vertically) and toward nature (horizontally).

Perception of self. There may also have been, as a result of the fall, a third type of reduction in perception in addition to the two already described. It is possible that Adam's perception of himself, his own "proprioception," giving him knowledge of the state of his own body, also became numbed or reduced. For there are now large and important parts of the vegetative nervous system which do not report directly to the higher central nervous system, but remain underground most of our normal lives. Bowel movement and heartbeat rate are today beyond the conscious control of most people. It is reported that some mystics as well as yogis claim to be able to consciously control these now normally vegetative functions. This, if true, might mean that they are recovering a function which has in the intervening years been lost or reduced. It is therefore possible that not only vertical and horizontal perception have been throttled since the fall, but internal bodily proprioception has been as well. Man has become partially "anesthetized."

Reduction Valve Inserted

As man's lines of communication with Mind-at-Large, with nature, and with himself through his nervous system, became constricted with the fall, a "reduction valve" was inserted, which hindered the free passage of perception from ultimate reality, and from nature, to man's consciousness.

Obviously this insertion of a "reduction valve" into the perceptive lines of communication produced a profound effect on the nature of Adam's mind, for the mind is nourished by such perception. Adam, the unfallen, joyfully perceiving God and infinity as well as material nature, was a vastly different creature from the fallen Adam lying to and fleeing from the Presence. Adam, the unfallen, was a joyous king, a true lord of the earth. Adam, the fallen, fleeing one, was immeasurably reduced in intellectual, perceptive capacity. C. S. Lewis and other authors believe that, at the fall, Adam's race became so reduced in the perception of reality, so shriveled and shrunken, that one could speak of a "loss of species," not merely a degradation, as having taken place at the fall. The glorious Adam before the fall, possessing a mind in unhindered communion with God, man, beast and himself, was hardly the same being who later fled at the sound of God's voice and lied in an attempt to cover up his tracks. He who could formerly think with his Creator now descends to the puerile attempt to hide his shame with sewn fig leaves.

Christ as True Picture of First Adam

The true picture of the pristine brilliance of the human race can be better conceived in the clear picture given us of the second Man, or the last Adam, who is a quickening Spirit from heaven. Christ, the last Adam, as he was seen on the Mount of Transfiguration before his death, gives us a true image of unfallen man. The various descriptions of our Lord after his resurrection conjure up in our mind's eye the type of beings the redeemed believers will be when they receive their resurrection bodies at Christ's coming, and when redeemed humanity recovers its now lost species. For it is Christ, the last Adam, who is going to restore to Adam's race the position it once held and lost in Eden.[6]

Biological Survival

Huxley does not, of course, see the reduction of man's

ability to perceive the infinite, or nature, as a consequence of the fall, but rather as a necessity for biological survival in this present jungle of a world. The important point for us is to see that modern scientists such as Dr. Huxley regard contemporary man as largely cut off from a consciousness of reality about him as well as within him, although he is theoretically capable of perceiving much more of it than he does at present. There is a width of ultimate Mind without and proprioception within from which he has been cut off—with which he normally cannot commune today. This observation is important:

> In so far as we are animals, our business is at all costs to survive. To make biological survival possible, Mind-at-Large has to be funnelled through the reducing valve of the brain and nervous system. What comes out the other end is a measly trickle of the kind of consciousness which will help us to stay alive.[7]

One cannot fail to note how well these ideas line up with Old Testament and New Testament teaching on the inability of fallen man to see God and live. Undimmed perception of the eternal Presence in our present condition and estate would consume us, according to the Bible. Translated into Dr. Huxley's language, this seems to be perfectly reasonable. For the shock of perceiving Mind-at-Large (or God) would so overwhelm us that we would not be able to deal adequately with it while carrying on the daily grind for physical survival. The prophets, when overwhelmed by the Glory, and falling at his feet as if dead, usually remembered one panacea for their dire troubles at such times. They brought coals from off the fire at the altar which purged their sins, making them capable of standing the flood of divine perception to which they were being exposed.[8]

Prerequisite for Perception

Purging of sin. Purgation of sin was the vital prerequisite for perception of eternity without dire consequences. The purged man and unfallen Adam had no difficulty with such perception, but unpurged fallen man was simply consumed in the fire of this perception. Therefore, to protect man in his fallen, unpurged state from perception of the Divine, became a vital necessity. The "reducing valve" was introduced and inserted between reality and Adam's perception. Open communion between Mind-at-Large and the human race had to be prevented or it would have destroyed fallen man. In his sinful state man could not see (fully perceive) God and live. Thus man's loss of the knowledge of eternal things started with the fall. The loss has become deeper, more profound, as the ages in the fallen state have progressed, so much so that Christ asked whether faith (in God and things beyond) would exist at all by the time of his second coming.[9] Would the lamp of perception of things hidden to physical sight have gone out entirely and forever? But the first Adam did not subsist on any such "measly trickle" of consciousness. Nor will the last Adam, the second Man from heaven. It goes without saying that the redeemed of the first Adam's race will not so subsist either, when the time of their redemption approaches.[10]

Further constriction. The corollary to this is contingent upon the purging we have mentioned above. It is seldom treated today, being out of fashion in most circles. The Old Testament and the New Testament are unanimous in declaring that the lusts of the flesh and of the mind "war against the soul."[11] If we take the "soul" to be man's "trickle" of conscious ego or personality, then the fulfilled lusts of the flesh and the mind damage and cut off our "soul," or personality, from communion with God (Mind-at-Large), thus reducing its function and consciousness to an even more "measly trickle." For the personality which was apparently constructed to live in conscious fellowship with God shrivels without this contact. If our ego still manages to function, though it receives only the present "measly trickle" of consciousness from Reality, what will happen when it receives even less of a "trickle" because of the further constriction of the "reducing valve"? If the fall caused the "insertion" of the "reducing valve" originally, further sin (further "fall") will cause further constriction of the passageway between ultimate Reality and us, choking the life line of the ego still more.

Thus, every sin or act of unbelief results in cutting us off still further from a consciousness or perception of the Infinite. Consciousness of the Reality of realities must, in consequence, be crushed under an increasing weight of sin. Romans 1 refers to this process as that of being given over to a reprobate mind (consciousness or conscience?) as a consequence of willful, habitual sin.

Reverse holds true. The reverse will also hold true, of course. The purging of sin by God's forgiveness in Christ will nourish and strengthen the ego in its perception of Reality. The Old and the New Testaments both describe how once a man settles down in comfort and affluence to serve himself, forgetting his higher God-given calling as a pilgrim and stranger on earth, he must progressively lose his perception of God or Mind-at-Large. His "reduction valve" becomes progressively more constricted by selfish egoism, as when "every man sat under his own fig tree and forgot the Lord his God." Sin, exclusively, or excessive self-interest caused the introduction of the "reducing valve" in the first place, and further application of sin further constricts the "valve." The consequence is that it is impossible to settle down to a life of pleasant selfishness, even of the "harmless" lethargic type of pious Lot in Sodom, and still retain Abraham's beatific vision and communication with Mind-at-Large. Abraham, in choosing the tent rather than the city, chose a kind of asceticism or self-discipline—and maintained the vision.

A man may have the very best intentions and even assume the most conservative position doctrinally, so that his "statement of faith" (to use the modern jargon of some conservative Christian circles) may be unexceptionable, yet a few years of ease, assured position, influence and other food for the ego, will as surely cut him off from the heavenly vision as Adam was cut off at the fall and Lot was cut off at

Sodom. Even the polite lusts of the flesh are as damaging here as heretical doctrine. C. S. Lewis described the process in his *Screwtape Letters*, the victims being classified as "spoiled saints."[12]

Gradually, imperceptibly, without any sudden crisis in their lives, the spoiled ones lose their vision, by increasing constriction of their "reducing valves" leading to the Reality of realities, and become fit "food" for Screwtape and his fellow tempters.

THE NATURE OF THE MIND

The Theory of the Contraction of the Field of Consciousness

Developed by Pierre Janet. These ideas on the eliminative function of the nervous system have received some confirmation from a rather unexpected quarter. Pierre Janet, who developed the theory of the contraction of the field of consciousness in the psychoanalytical school, has explained, with the help of this theory, the genesis of neuroses.[13]

The basic postulate behind this idea of the contraction of the field of consciousness is really quite simple. A person does something, or indulges in thought about something, of which his conscience deeply disapproves. His activities give rise to guilt feelings, which are, of course, unpleasant to him. He reacts to this unpleasant guilt feeling by repressing all thoughts and memories of the painful matter; he bans them from his mind. That is, he voluntarily contracts the field of his own consciousness by banning conscious thought in certain areas unpleasant to him. By this process he eliminates part or parts of his field of consciousness. This means simply that he contracts his field of consciousness in general when he suppresses certain fields of thought in it. A person who represses wide areas of thought because they are unpleasant to him, suffers, in the course of time, from a more restricted consciousness than he had before the repression began.

Repressed thought not destroyed. However, a repressed field of consciousness is not the same thing as a destroyed or eliminated field of consciousness. The repressed tendencies or thoughts are not eliminated. They return as memories, dreams, disguised as mental pictures, or as neurotic symptoms, paralyses, obsessions and even functional disorders. These facts agree with biblical doctrine, though the Bible simply calls the unpleasant offenses against one's conscience "sin."

If we repress sin, then, on this basis the repression will bring with it a reduction in our field of consciousness. The result of this is that, in this repressed area, we no longer will have any consciousness at all. We feel the unpleasantness no longer, for we have forced it down to the unconscious level of the mind. In the unpleasant areas concerned we will have nothing but general anesthesia, total numbness. This is what the Bible describes as having eyes that see not, ears that hear not and hearts that do not understand.[14] In the subject area in which we have repressed or put out of mind, we are benumbed. And the wider the area in which we have repressed, the more general will be our insensitiveness, blindness, deafness and lack of understanding.

Increasing insensitiveness. This is why the practice of any sin against our own conscience must, in the course of time, make us increasingly insensitive to the sinfulness of the sin. Most crimes are hard to carry out the first time, be they stealing or murdering one's fellowmen. But practice makes perfect—and insensitive. The Nazis gassed millions of Jews with as little compunction as the average person has when he kills a fly. No doubt the first gassings a concentration camp commandant carried out upset him. But this wore off with time. In the area of the sinfulness of murder, the field of consciousness contracts or shrinks until the murderers no longer notice the unpleasant feeling connected with it. They became completely anesthetized in this and related areas. Our hearts become gradually the more hardened; our eyes slowly become the more blind the more we practice repression of guilt. The deafness of our understanding ears becomes the more profound, the further we go into practicing sin against our conscience.

Need for education. Of course, our conscience may be wrong, for it needs continual education. Nevertheless, if we sin against it, even though it is wrongly oriented, a repression occurs, with all its consequences. For this reason it is vital to educate and instruct our conscience within the lines laid down by the Bible. This will bring with it sensitivity to those wide areas in which we, in this life, so badly need instruction, and in which God's Spirit is active and sensitive.

Years ago my conscience forbade me to do certain things, though I can do them today with the inward conviction that they are right. My conscience has learned, I trust, to see things more in the light of God's Word, compared with my views in younger days. Similarly, I could do things then which I could not think of doing today. My conscience has changed positively as well as negatively.

But no matter what the state of development of the conscience may be, it is important not to repress its judgments. If one rides roughshod over the conscience, then repression, followed by contraction of the field of consciousness, must occur. We must constantly test our conscience with the Bible, so that our judgments become more and more aligned to those of the Bible and no unnecessary repressions arise, with their consequences.

Confirms eliminative function. Thus the theory of the contraction of the field of consciousness as an explanation of the origin of neuroses, confirms at the same time the eliminative function of the central nervous system. For as more and more consciousness fields are eliminated, the more an individual represses sin into the unconscious mind. This is merely another way of saying that the constriction of the "reducing valve" connecting our minds with Mind-at-Large will become tighter and narrower the further we fall into sin. Romans 1 maintains just the same principle when it teaches that if a man is capable of seeing the design in nature without being thankful to the Designer, his mind will become darkened and his thoughts futile.

Corrective measure. As all of must have found it impossible to live up to our own standards, let alone those of the Bible, the outlook for our mental health would appear to be bleak and the prognosis for neurosis strong. It is important to remember, then, as a corrective measure, that just as the field of consciousness can be restricted by repression, so it can also be broadened by the opposite process. That is, to face up to and deal with offenses against God's or our own law, instead of repressing the offenses, will widen our field of consciousness.

Bringing offenses to the light, that is to Christ, confessing them, asking for forgiveness and cleansing from our guilt by Christ's vicarious death for us—this will bring widening of our field of consciousness. For in this way we shall become more sensitive to more subjects in which both our consciences and God's Spirit are sensitive. By confessing our offenses to Christ and receiving his forgiveness, we will increase our awareness and consciousness of wider fields in everyday experience. Our "viewfinder" looking out onto life will become enlarged, which means we will experience more of life, including its joys, and perhaps its sorrows. And the "field" will be not only enlarged, it will also be "brightened," for sensitivity as well as width or largeness are increased.

This is why the experience of forgiveness of sins and of the new birth makes even the trees seem greener, the skies more blue and our friends more compatible! For our experience is intensified. The new birth gives a boost to the experience of consciousness by bringing sin to the surface, to the light of Christ, where it is dealt with instead of being repressed. We might almost maintain that the new birth and the forgiveness of sins are truly "psychedelic" experiences, for they enlarge and deepen our field of consciousness and expand our experience of God and of life.

Analogy with the Computer

Internal and external needs. The brain has often been compared with the modern computer and the computer with the brain.[15] There is much to support the analogy, particularly if C. D. Broad's and Henri Bergson's views of perception are kept in mind. For the computer is not in itself basically creative. It works on a program with which it must be supplied by an exogenous mind and in a language which it, as a machine, can handle. Yet it performs its own internal processes. The computer must have intimate access to the reality of a creative mind outside of itself to set its problems and programs, if it is to function properly. But this does not exclude the computer's own internal, individual activity.

The computer's input is fed by means of a "reducing valve" in the form of a computer language and program. This restricted input channel is its sole contact with its "ultimate reality," that is, with the person whose mind is programing the machine. The machine "feeds" on the exogenous reality of its program. The more the "reducing valve" is constricted, the more the language fed into it is simplified and restricted, the narrower the range of the problems the machine can tackle, and the more the machine's "consciousness" is reduced. The richer the input language the machine is capable of digesting, the less the "reducing valve" connecting the machine to its ultimate reality (the programing mind) is constricted and the greater the potential "consciousness" of the machine becomes with respect to the mind programing and nourishing it, and the problems this mind sets it to solve.

This all boils down to the proposition that the "consciousness" of the computer is dependent on the input via the program, plus its own spontaneous internal activity. Now, if the input from the exogenous mind is greatly reduced by the "restricting valve," a point will be reached where nothing sensible can be made of this message at all. The weaker the "measly input trickle" becomes, the more it will have to be amplified. But with greater amplification, the more decisive the "noise" from entirely internal sources within the computer will become.

Modern man in similar position. It seems that modern man has long since reached a comparable position. No personal, reliable message is transmitted through his blunted perception to aid in the functioning of his "computer" in its communication with Mind-at-Large. The "message" is so weak, the valve so constricted by generations of sin, that the amplification factor, and with it the "noise" from his internal spontaneous functioning, has become so magnified that the whole race hears only the chaos of internal noise instead of messages from Mind-at-Large. But it does seem in some cases that drugs and other means can be capable of truly expanding our "measly trickle" of communication from outside. That is, there are psychedelic means available for increasing external perceptive ability.

Infinity of the Mind

It is clear that the brain, as such, is a highly complex organ—far more complex than any computer ever conceived by man. It is also exceedingly compact. Its fuel demands are modest, it is satisfied to live off the land on cabbage, carbohydrates and chops. But the actual circuitry of the brain, although enormously complex, is by no means infinitely so. In line with this, the calculations the brain can carry out, having been supplied with data, are also complex, but not infinitely so, for they are limited in speed and quantity.

Time is necessity. The brain needs time to work. One thought *follows* another through its mechanisms and circuits. If one were to cut out the flow of time which the brain uses to guide the sequence of its impulses one after another in time, it would be difficult indeed to envisage any brain function at all. That is, the normal functioning of the brain as a computer is governed by time and by the ordinary laws of physics, chemistry and physiology. How it functions as a console—at which Mind-at-Large presides over our personalities, giving perception of Reality—escapes any sure knowledge today.

In the ordinary course of events, therefore, the brain needs a liberal amount of time to lubricate its mechanism. This makes the physiological organ we know as the brain a product of finiteness, subject to the second law of thermodynamics and to the ordinary laws of physics and biochemistry. It is certainly not eternal in this aspect. On this basis physiologists and materialists have rightly regarded the brain as a perfectly typical, ordinary physiological organ.

Door to eternity. And yet, it is also the door to eternity in man: "Also he has put *eternity* into man's mind, yet so that he cannot find out what God has done from the beginning to the end." [16] That is, the brain may mediate nervous impulses in time according to known laws. But it also mediates the thoughts of eternity to us, according to entirely unknown laws. This side of the problem of the brain's activities is examined more fully later.

This difference between the physiological, oxygen-consuming organ known as the brain and the seat of man's ego (or mind) where he crystallizes his thoughts of eternity, brings into focus the problem of distinguishing between the two entities: the physiological oxygen-consuming brain and the mind as the seat of thought. Some physiologists and psychologists speak, therefore, of the "brain-mind" in order to avoid the distinction.[17] Nevertheless, although the thought life is certainly mediated by the brain, there is little certain evidence that no thought could exist without the brain, as later sections show.

Similarly, although a computer is a purely electrical machine governed by the ordinary laws of mechanics and electricity, yet it may handle and nourish itself on exogenous *creative* thought governed, perhaps, by entirely different laws outside its own dimensions. The brain is also a perfectly normal physiological organ, but it can handle and solve purely theoretical problems having nothing to do with the laws of physiology governing it. A computer which does not itself function according to laws of, for example, biological enzymology, can nevertheless solve problems in biological enzymology. The brain must be regarded in itself, therefore, as a passing, finite temporal organ. But it can nevertheless be also the mediator of Mind-at-Large, the supranatural or the eternal, whose governing laws have nothing to do with the physiological laws governing neural functions.

The following paragraphs are intended to demonstrate some "extra functions" exhibited and handled by the physiological brain, which may be difficult to explain on a purely physiological basis.

Pilot's Experience

Some years ago I read of a pilot who took off one frosty winter morning from a private airstrip in his own single-motor sports plane. Just as he became airborne at about twenty feet, his single motor cut out. At this precise instant he remembered (though I cannot vouch for exact details) his instructor's reiterated warnings to never try to turn back to the airstrip under such circumstances. He had insufficient altitude to attempt any turn, but had to keep going straight ahead.

In front of him lay a cabbage patch. He had to aim for this and hope that his wheels would not sink too far into the soft earth and turn him up on his nose. Then his wife's warning and pleadings to give up his flying activities flashed through his mind. The eyes of his children looking anxiously at him when their mother talked to him about these things came vividly to mind. His parents, his parents-in-law, as well as many childhood scenes passed before him. He remembered his pet dog as a child, the romps he had had with his faithful animal. Some urgent business problems came into his consciousness and retreated. They were followed by some conversations he had with his business associates.

All the time he was aiming at the cabbage patch a few feet below him, frosty and glistening in the early morning sunlight. Then the question of whether his life insurance company would pay his wife so that she could educate the children, should he crash and be killed, flashed through his mind. Yes, he decided, it was a good company, he could rely on them. All these thoughts and scenes passed like a color film in front of his eyes—and it was a good full-length stereo film too, so vivid did it appear to the pilot.

Then suddenly, right in the middle of the "film showing," his motor cut in again and the plane began to gain altitude. He circled once, then landed and walked over to his mechanic to report the defect.

The mechanic pooh-poohed the idea of defect, smiled and pointed out that the motor had misfired just once on all six cylinders (he had heard it), that is, for two revolutions. The carburetor jets were just a trifle small for cold weather. At about six thousand revolutions per minute the motor missed one firing stroke per cylinder, or faltered for two revolutions, a total time of 0.02 seconds during which the motor failed. Yet practically a lifetime of perception had passed through the pilot's brain in that 0.02 of a second.

This kind of experience is well known.[18] In emergencies or in the face of death the brain seems to function without or with less of the normal time component. That is, it becomes quasi-timeless. As we have already seen, under the influence of a number of hallucinatory drugs a similar phenomenon can occur. The time relationship factor governing the functioning of the brain seems to get out of focus. Perhaps it is at this point that the "eternity" placed in man's heart becomes a functional reality in man's "measly trickle" of consciousness.

Extrasensory Perception (ESP)

Personal experience. ESP is no longer as popular as it used to be in some scientific circles, nevertheless, the following personal experience may be of interest. While we were living in Norway at Tertnes, near Bergen, our third child was born. When he was a few weeks old, my brother and his family of five little girls came to stay with us on their vacation. The girls, especially the youngest, a three-year-old, were delighted with the new baby and were with him as much as possible. Since the youngest was simply fascinated by him and was always stealing upstairs to where he lay, we had to keep a continual watch over the baby.

One evening my wife and I had to go to Bergen to a royal

reception with King Olaf of Norway. Before leaving at 7 P.M., we instructed our reliable German nurse to keep a sharp eye on the baby and the youngest girl, even at the expense of not doing other chores. At 7:10 P.M. we were just descending the hairpin bend leading from Tertnes (it was a gravel road, tricky in wet or frosty weather) to the main road to Bergen, when my wife suddenly called out, "Stop! We must go back home at once!" We slithered to a halt on the gravel road as I inquired the reason behind the sudden, unusual command. My wife was almost in a state of shock and answered something about the baby. I was just preparing to turn the car around on the hairpin bend when my wife suddenly said that everything was all right now and we could proceed to Bergen. To my shame, I was greatly put out by my wife's performance, but proceeded to Bergen.

When we arrived home at about 9:30 P.M., I took the nurse aside before she spoke to my wife, and asked her to tell me exactly what had happened at 7:10 P.M. She colored at my question with its specific mention of time and then told me that she had heard little footsteps upstairs soon after we had left. She had gone upstairs immediately, finding my three-year-old niece with our baby. The little girl had already pulled him off his cot by his legs and was in the process of dragging him by his feet toward the head of the stairs to bump him down them to show him to the rest of the family. The nurse had rescued him just at 7:10 P.M.

Artificial experiments. If this is an example of what is known as sporadic extrasensory perception, then I believe the phenomenon is fairly common. It is a far cry, of course, from this sort of perception to the rather artificial guessing experiments one reads about in psychical research journals, which are so heavily criticized today because of technique and controls. Personally, I do not think one could control satisfactorily an *experiment* involving a mother's sporadic perception of her baby's real needs in real danger, for this must be, in the very nature of things, an uncontrollable event. The perception involved in the usual ESP experiments makes use of hypothetical or artificial nonsporadic, controlled attempts at perception. In the case of a mother and her child, infinitely stronger ties—psychical ties—are involved, which are unfortunately practically impossible to control experimentally. Thus our experience at Tertnes would probably carry a low rating in a psychical expert's estimation, for it could not be experimentally controlled. Yet I pass it on here, because my wife and I were both surprised by it and can both vouch for it. It certainly appears to illustrate that the brain is not *merely* a computer run according to *known* physiological laws.

Not "radio" perception. The explanation of this type of perception cannot, of course, be that there was a sort of "radio" perception or communication between my wife and our baby, for the baby would scarcely have possessed the "wattage" to have reached us in the mountains, where we were well screened from our house by intervening hills. Further, if electromagnetic waves of any sort were concerned, perception of this type ought to get weaker as the distance between the communicating parties increases. But, in spite of what the psychical experimentalists report about the contradictory effects of distance on their ESP experiments,[19] it is believed in many circles that, where cases of perception are concerned which come into the same or similar category as that experienced by my wife, distance has little importance.

My father-in-law's mother knew the exact time that her son was wounded in World War I—and said so at the time, before the official news came in. Apparently she did not know precisely what had happened, but merely that it was something serious. Her son was many miles away at the western front at the time. As far as I can gather, perceptive communication of this type seems to take place between persons who are bound together by close spiritual and personal ties. The very nature of these ties would preclude fitting them into any controlled artificial experiment. Guessing card numbers would measure an entirely different psychical property with little relation to the kind of psychical ties between mother and child. A number is a clear thought entity and in principle, therefore, different from the mere malaise which came over my wife (or my father-in-law's mother) about their sons' fate. Neither knew precisely what had happened, though some subjects seem to know when death or another grave event has been involved. A card number is a rather different and more precise matter.

Conclusions. What conclusions can one draw if electromagnetic signals obeying the normal laws of physics are ruled out by indifference to distance and other physical barriers? Would a reasonable conclusion be that the brain or other organ in the body possesses faculties of thought perception, particularly toward Mind-at-Large, which are at present unknown or outside of the laws which we recognize as governing our physical universe of three dimensions and time? If the mind is normally, though tenuously, in contact with Mind-at-Large, an "echo" might be "reflected" from Mind-at-Large into other minds with which it is in contact, thus establishing ESP.

As mentioned above, official psychical evaluation of the above experiences would probably carry a low rating. Dr. Hansel would look for a lapse of memory or a tendency to worry unduly on the part of my wife as an explanation of the phenomenon. Douglas Blackburn and his colleagues rightly believed they would "doubtless raise a storm of protest when [they] assert that the principle cause of belief in psychical phenomena is the inability of the average man to observe accurately and estimate the value of evidence, plus a bias in favour of the phenomenon being real."[20] But the world has proceeded a long way since Blackburn's time toward materialism and away from any belief in the supernatural. Scientists as a whole, particularly biological scientists, are becoming more and more unable to believe in anything supernatural. There are certain notable exceptions, chiefly among physicists and mathematicians. Accordingly, now that the experimental technique used in certain early psychical research card-guessing experiments had been shown to yield unrepeatable results, the conclusion is almost foregone that no credibility at all is to be given to any so-called psychic phenomena. Added to this are the many cases of fraud by mediums said to be possessed of psychic powers who have been exposed in common trickery and cheating time and time again.

[1] Sir James Jeans, *The Mysterious Universe,* pp. 154, 158-59.
[2] Aldous Huxley, *Doors of Perception;* C.D. Broad, *Scientific Thought,* pp. 529-31; Henri Bergson, *Matter and Memory.*
[3] Broad as cited by Huxley, pp. 22-23.
[4] Eccles. 3:11.
[5] Gen. 3:1-19.
[6] I Cor. 15:45.
[7] Huxley, p. 23.
[8] Isa. 6:6.
[9] Luke 18:8.
[10] I Cor. 15:45.
[11] I Peter 2:11; I John 2:16; Mark 4:19; Ps. 32:3, 5; 38:1-22; 41:4; Prov. 14:34.
[12] C.S. Lewis, *The Screwtape Letters and Screwtape Proposes a Toast,* p. 103.
[13] See Paul Tournier, *The Healing of Persons,* p. 54.
[14] Matt. 13:13.
[15] Cf. Harold E. Hatt, *Cybernetics and the Image of Man.*
[16] Eccles. 3:11 (RSV).
[17] Samuel Bogoch, *The Biochemistry of Memory,* pp. 5, 13.
[18] On the other hand, ordinary dreams and other thinking processes are thought to take place usually at ordinary speed: 'Instantaneous dreams in which the events of a lifetime flash through the mind in a few seconds are very popular in folklore. There is very little evidence that such high-velocity dreams occur and considerable evidence that they do not. . . . The general finding is that the time course in dreams is much the same as in real life. . . . Very speedy dreams might occur of exceptional mental ability." Professor A. C. Aitken of Edinburgh was "a most remarkable lightning calculator . . . and . . . claimed to be able to experience the whole of a passage of music, which would normally take half an hour, in a space of half a minute or less. A lightning calculator might have dreams of lightning speed, but the ordinary person who thinks at ordinary speed seems to dream at ordinary speed as well." Thus the normal waking and sleeping processes of the brain ordinarily take place at ordinary speed. The "flash" processes under stress are obviously exceptional, though vouched for. (Citations from *The Anatomy of Sleep,* pp. 71-72.)

In his book *Matière et Mémoire* Henri Bergson (English trans., *Matter and Memory*, p. 200) states: "But there is nothing more instructive in this regard than what happens in cases of sudden suffocation, in men drowned or hanged. The man, when brought to life again, states that he saw, in a very short time, all the forgotten events of his life passing before him with great rapidity, with their smallest circumstances and in the very order in which they occurred." Cf. Forbes Winslow, *Obscure Diseases of the Brain,* pp. 25 ff.; Ribot, *Maladies de la Mémoire,* pp. 139 ff.; Mauro, *Le Sommeil et les Reves,* p. 439. All are cited by Bergson, p. 200.

19Cf. C.E.M. Hansel, *ESP, A Scientific Evaluation,* pp. 193, 239. Hansel states that, with respect to the relationship of distance to ESP, not a single lawful interrelationship appears to have been established: "How, for example, does distance affect extra-sensory-perception? The relationship between scoring rate and distance is completely chaotic, apparently dependent on the investigator, the subject and the experimental conditions. . . . Extra-sensory-perception is not a fact but a theory put forward to account for observations consisting of high scores. . . . However, a theory that fails to account for a variety of facts and that cannot predict what will happen in further tests, is of no value."

20Douglas Blackburn, *Daily News,* London (Sept. 1, 1911), as cited by *ibid.,* p. 193.

9. Psychic Phenomena

MEDIUMISTIC SEANCES

Personally I do not think that real, transcendental perception could prostitute itself to the trivial mummery often reported as having occurred in mediumistic seances—curtains blowing, "kissing" by "spirits" through curtains, ringing of bells, playing of guitars in half-darkened rooms, touching by "spirit hands" reaching out from the darkness, startling and unaccountable raps and bangs. Nor do I think that the often ambiguous information "reported" by controls from the purported realms of the dead are in many cases much more than mockery and taking mean advantage of those who have lost their loved ones. The famous magician Harry Houdini spent nearly a lifetime exposing such matters.

Nevertheless, it must be remembered that the very fact that a counterfeit currency exists (fake dollars, pounds sterling or rubles) proves that real dollars, pounds sterling or rubles exist. The counterfeit would be no counterfeit if the real, the genuine, did not exist. The counterfeit's existence is dependent on the fact that the genuine exists too. There is, as we have already said, evidence ad nauseam that perhaps the majority of "psychical" phenomena reek of counterfeit, often cheap counterfeit. But is this not excellent evidence at the same time that the real and genuine must exist too? Anyone interested in some of the frauds that have presented their claims to psychical powers should read C. E. M. Hansel's account.[1] But, in spite of all the exposure of the fraudulent, we would be giving a truly one-sided and therefore untrue picture of psychical phenomena if we did not refer at the same time to the evidence for the genuine and the real.

EVIDENCE FOR PSYCHICAL ACTIVITY

Aside from the widespread frauds in psychical research which Dr. Hansel and others so rightly expose, there are aspects of this subject which other equally careful researchers have found both inexplicable and impossible to ignore. Such workers have produced carefully sifted evidence which leads them to opposite conclusions to those reached by Dr. Hansel. No one experienced in exact methods and careful sorting of evidence will doubt the unimpeachable evidence resulting from work carried out during a lifetime with persevering care by the eminent Cambridge philosopher and psychical research worker Dr. C. D. Broad of Trinity College. Although Dr. Broad may perhaps be classified as a skeptic he has produced evidence for psychical phenomena which our present knowledge of physical sciences has not yet explained. In one of Dr. Broad's recent works some preliminary chapters are devoted to describing the methods used to preclude error and counterfeit, after which evidence is presented for many types of psychic phenomena which are unaccountable on the ordinary physical basis of life, science, and the brain.[2]

One such section of Dr. Broad's book is devoted to "The S.P.R.'s [Society for Psychical Research] 'Census of Hallucinations,'" in which so-called sporadic cases (rather than experimental phenomena) of phantasms are described. An hallucinatory experience of perceiving another person not actually physically present but alive elsewhere is classified as a "phantasm of the living." Similarly, an hallucinatory perception of a person known to be dead is classified as "phantasm of the dead." An experience of regarding one's own body as separated from oneself, either sleeping or unconscious, whereas one's ego is active and conscious, is designated as an "out-of-the-body experience." Surprising as it may seem to the skeptic, Dr. Broad, who is obviously exceptionally well read in the sciences, ancient languages and philosophy, as well as in matters purely psychical, produces well-authenticated examples of each type of phantasm.

In view of the light these examples throw on the nature of the human mind, and therefore on the possible effects of drugs upon it, it is proposed herewith to mention a few of these examples and so to emphasize the fact that there is often as excellent evidence for matters psychical as there is for matters purely physical, though the evidence may necessarily be of a different kind.

SPORADIC CASES[3]

Phantasms of the Living

Mr. H was a freight inspector on the old London and North Western Railway, England, and was on duty on a freight train on the night of April 16, 1902. Mrs. H was at home with a sick baby. Before going to bed she put a glass of water on the table in case the sick child should be thirsty during the night. At 3 A.M. she awoke herself, being thirsty; as she drank, she was surprised to see in the glass of water a moving picture of a freight car and a caboose in the rear. The cars smashed into the caboose and damaged it badly. At 9 A.M. her husband returned home safe and well. She reported her experience to him immediately and learned from him that an accident has taken place at about 10 P.M. During the night he had passed the scene of the accident twice, once at 3:10 A.M. and again at 7:50 A.M. Some cars had indeed badly damaged a caboose.

A very well-attested case reported by Dr. Broad concerns the novelist Rider Haggard, and his dog Bob. Mr. Haggard had suffered a nightmare on the night of July 9, 1904, in which he dreamed that his black retriever dog, Bob, was lying on its side in rough undergrowth beside water. Mr. Haggard felt as if he were in some way issuing from the dog's body and that the dog was trying to speak to him and tell him that it was dying. Mrs. Haggard woke him at this point in the nightmare because he was making such awful noises. The time was about 2 A.M. on July 10. The story of the nightmare was repeated again at breakfasttime on July 10 and everyone laughed. That evening it was noticed that Bob was missing. On July 14 Mr. Haggard and his groom found Bob's body floating in the river Waveney against a small dam at Falcon Bridge, Bungay. It was already very decomposed, its skull had been fractured in three places, and both forelegs broken. At first it was thought that the dog had been caught in a trap. Actually two railway plate layers reported that the dog had been killed by a train. They showed Mr. Haggard the evidence of the train accident at a bridge over the river. From this it was deduced that the July 9 excursion train which left Ditchingham at 10:25 P.M., in the direction of Bungay, had in fact killed the dog which fell onto the bank of the river. Dr. Broad comments on the full report that this is one of the most curious and also one of the best documented of the sporadic cases.[4]

Another well-attested case of a sporadic phantasm concerns Lieutenants McConnel and Larkin, both flying officers of the RAF, and good friends. McConnel had been sent on a mission to deliver an aircraft to another station and was to return immediately in an accompanying aircraft. Both planes were overtaken by fog and, after his companion's plane had landed safely, McConnel crashed and was killed instantly. His watch had stopped at 3:25 P.M. on December 7, 1918. His friend, Lieutenant Larkin, who had remained at base during these operations, was sitting in front of the fire with his back to the door reading and smoking, when, between 3:15 and

3:30 P.M., he heard someone walking up the passage. He heard the door open noisily, after which McConnel's voice called out, "Hello, old boy."

We cite from Dr. Broad's account:

> Larkin turned half round in his chair, and was sure he saw McConnel standing in the doorway, half in and half out of the room, his hand holding the door knob. He was dressed in full flying kit, but wearing his naval cap. There was nothing unusual in his appearance. Larkin remarked: "Hello, back already?" The figure replied: "Yes, got there all right . . ." and added some such words as: ". . . had a good trip" — or ". . . a fine trip." Larkin was looking straight at him during this interchange. The figure then said: "Well, cheerio!" shut the door with a bang and went away.[5]

Lieutenant Garner-Smith entered at 3:45 P.M. and expressed the hope that McConnel would be back early, as they were due in Lincoln that evening. Larkin replied that McConnel was already back and had been in the room a few minutes earlier but had probably not yet had tea. Garner-Smith went out to look for McConnel. Later, Larkin was dumbfounded on hearing the facts of the fatal accident.

Dr. Broad points out that this report cannot be explained on the basis of mistaken identity because McConnel's voice and noisy manner were easily recognizable; and the naval cap, which McConnel had retained from his naval career, clinched the matter. Only two other men at the base at Scampton were in a position to wear such a uniform, and neither of them could be confused with McConnel.

A number of other interesting cases are reported by Dr. Broad in the work cited to which reference may be made.

Phantasms of the Dead

Under the heading "Phantasms of the Dead" Dr. Broad cites the now famous sporadic Chaffin Will case.[6] This case has been thoroughly attested to by the very competent people mentioned in the S.P.R. report.

The substance of the case is that James L. Chaffin, a North Carolina farmer, made a will on November 16, 1905, which was attested to by two witnesses and in which he left his farm to his third son, but nothing at all to his wife or his other three sons. After having read the story of Jacob's deception of his blind father Isaac in Genesis 27, he made another will on January 10, 1919, in which he divided his property equally among his four children and confided his wife, their mother, to their care. However, the second will was not attested nor its existence divulged to anyone during his lifetime. Mr. Chaffin then hid this second will in his father's family Bible at the Genesis 27 story, folding a sort of envelope to hold the will. He informed no one of this, but he wrote a note and stitched it into the inside pocket of an old overcoat. The note read: "Read the 27th chapter of Genesis in my daddie's old Bible."

Chaffin died on September 7, 1921, and the first will was probated afterward. The third son duly took over the farm until he died shortly afterward. In June, 1925, a surviving son, James Pinkney Chaffin, began to have vivid dreams of his father appearing silently at his bedside. Later on his father appeared to him again, pulled back the old black overcoat he was wearing, which was well known to the son, and said: "You will find my will in my overcoat pocket." Next morning James went to look for the overcoat at his mother's, but it had been given to his brother John, who lived some twenty miles away. On examination, he found the lining of the inside pocket sewn up. Inside he found a roll of paper, tied with string and bearing the following inscription in his father's handwriting: "Read the 27th chapter of Genesis in my daddie's old Bible."

Seeing the remarkable way things were developing, James called witnesses before taking further steps. The resultant findings are all sworn testimony. James and his witnesses found the dilapidated old Bible in an upper room and at the Genesis 27 story he found the second unattested will. In North Carolina, where these events took place, such a will can be judged valid if the supporting evidence is sufficient. In view of the witnesses' evidence from the time of the discovery of the paper in the overcoat onward, the second will was declared valid before a judge in the Superior Court of Davie County, North Carolina, in December, 1925.[7]

Experimental (Nonsporadic) Cases and Out-of-the-Body Experiences

Dr. Broad describes a number of experimental (i.e., nonsporadic) cases in which individuals have deliberately set out to produce hallucinatory quasi-perception experimentally in other persons at a distance. A Mr. Kirk was able, for instance, to cause a Miss G to have a quasi-perception of himself as though he were present in her room, when he was in reality some distance away in his own room.[8] The same author also describes well-attested "out of the body" and "lucid" experiences in which the dreamer knows that his physical body is asleep and in a different location from his own body.

The second type of experience, the "out of the body" kind, might possibly have some connection with that described by the Apostle Paul, during which he says he was caught up to the third heaven, to the paradise of God—whether in the body or out of the body he did not know—and heard things which cannot be repeated, which man may not utter.[9] The cases which Dr. Broad cites could confirm the apostle's experience, even though Paul's was on an infinitely higher plane.

Dr. Broad cites as authentic the case of Dr. X, an M.D. and Fellow of the Royal College of Physicians, who was asked to assist at the scene of a flying accident, but who himself crashed on the way. Dr. X testified afterward that he remembered nothing of the actual impact in the flying accident. He was thrown out of the cockpit and landed on his back, sustaining severe injuries which caused widespread paralysis. Immediately after the accident, his body showed no sign of consciousness; but Dr. X remembers looking down vertically on his body from about two hundred feet directly above it. He saw the brigadier, the lieutenant-colonel and the pilot running toward his body and remembers wondering why they were interested in it. [10] He also saw the ambulance start out for the scene of the accident, stall, and restart (the driver had to descend each time and crank the motor as there was no self-starter). The interesting point which Dr. Broad makes is, that Dr. X, from where he (or his body) lay in a hollow, could not possibly have seen all these things. But Dr. X distinctly remembers seeing the ambulance stall once more, the medical orderly rushing back to his hut to fetch something, and returning to the ambulance, which then started on its journey again. It is emphasized repeatedly that, from where his body lay in a hollow, Dr. X could not possibly have seen any of these events, even if he had been conscious, which he was not at the time they happened.

Dr. X remembers wondering about all the fuss. He then experienced traveling as far as Hazelbrouck, then moving toward Cornwall and the Atlantic. Finally he experienced a pull backward toward the vertical position directly above where his body lay. Suddenly he resumed normal consciousness and felt the orderly pouring sal-volatile down his throat. He was paralyzed in all four limbs, the diaphragm and the six lower ribs. He told the orderly that he must not be moved until expert medical help came. Dr. Abrahams of the RAMC, who treated Dr. X, wrote to the S.P.R. in 1956 and confirmed the details of the case.

Trance Mediumship

In the course of his lectures on psychical research Dr. Broad gives some interesting accounts of trance mediumship which are relevant to our interest in hallucinatory drug research. [11] As they throw light on the functioning of the mind in hallucination, we shall briefly investigate a few of the more interesting mediumship cases. In none of these cases were hallucinatory drugs used.

Produce no new reactions. It should be borne in mind that, in general, drugs produce no new reactions or symptoms in cells or organisms but merely accentuate in one direction or another natural cell or nervous phenomena. For example, hallucinations and dreams are normal nervous phenomena, but both can be accentuated or suppressed with suitable drug aid. So drugs need not be expected to produce anything new, even in hallucinatory phenomena. What happens with drug aid can happen also without drugs in a greater or lesser degree.

Mediumship, trance conditions and hallucinations are all manifestations as old as man, as far as one can tell from ancient writings. Even in ancient times the use of drugs in accentuating or suppressing these conditions was known empirically. Medicine men well knew how to use certain mushrooms and other plant products to help in the production of hallucinations, as we have already seen. Very recent work has refined the scope of drugs. Certain trancelike states can be produced almost at will with substances like LSD. In view of the present drug epidemic and its hallucinations and other accompanying phenomena, it is important for us to know what is really happening in this respect so as to be in a position to perceive the significance of the epidemic seen in contemporary society.

Two types of mediumship. Dr. Broad distinguishes two types of mediumship. First "ostensible possession," by which he means mediumship in which the control-persona "possesses" the medium. This represents trance mediumship of the more usual kind. It is sometimes described by psychical research workers as "telergic." During this type of mediumship the personality of the medium is entirely ousted by the ostensible control-persona. The medium speaks, writes and shows mannerisms resembling those of the person whose departed spirit she ostensibly represents.

There is also the telepathic type of mediumship, which is much less common than the telergic type. During this mediumship, the medium is in a more or less normal state, certainly not in a deep trance in which her personality has been ousted by the control-persona. In such cases the medium is able to read the minds of ostensible communicators from the spirit world. In telergy, in which the medium's personality is temporarily ousted and the body taken over by the control-persona, the latter uses the physical organs belonging to the medium as though they were temporarily its own. Thus, a medium in a telergic trance will suddenly speak with the voice of man or a little child, according to the personality of the ostensible possessing persona. In the telepathic type of mediumship, "telesthesia," or telepathy, takes place, but no "possession." The ostensible communicator is supposed to operate by causing a "quasi-sensation," image, idea, impulse or emotion directly in the medium's mind. Thus the medium will use her normal voice organs to transmit the message which she has read by telepathic means in the ostensible communicator's "mind."

Concerning the first, or telergic type of mediumship, Dr. Broad reports from personal experience how disconcerting it can be to hear what seems to be the voice of an elderly man with an elaborately academic manner issuing from the lips of a woman medium, who, a moment before, had been speaking with the voice of a little girl.[12] This he classifies as "ostensible possession" and describes it as the condition in which the medium has lost control of her own body and yielded it temporarily to the control of the allegedly departed spirit.

Mediumship cases. Although in recent years mediumship has become connected with spiritualism and often, unfortunately, with fraud, the mediumships of Mrs. Leonard, Mrs. Willett (Mrs. Combe-Tennant) and Mrs. Warren Elliott stand out above this level in their integrity. These three mediumships have been investigated by the most stringent procedures. Dr. Broad comes to important theoretical conclusions as a result of the evidence he uncovers, so that a look into the mediumship of these ladies may be rewarding.

Mrs. Leonard was the classical telergic type of medium who possessed a single control and a number of ostensible communicators associated with various sitters. Her regular control called herself Feda and is referred to in Dr. Broad's account as the Feda-persona.

Mrs. Willett (otherwise known as Mrs. Combe-Tennant) was a highly educated lady, a nonprofessional medium who took a prominent part in public affairs and who was made a justice of the peace in 1920. She was the first woman to be appointed, in 1922, by the British government as a delegate to the assembly of the League of Nations. Her distinguished mediumship is thus proof that this faculty is not always associated with an uneducated, uncritical mind or with cheap fraud. Her husband Charles Combe-Tennant owned large holdings of land and Cadoxton Lodge, Neath. Other members of her family were distinguished in scholastic and other fields.

Mrs. Willett did not usually experience the normal type of trance, followed by telergic possession by the ostensible communicator-persona and the ousting of her own personality. She received "silent daylight impressions" when she was by herself and in a practically normal state of consciousness. Some psychical research workers designate this as a telepathic type of mediumship, as already pointed out. In this state she received impressions of definitely worded messages. Sometimes she was aware of certain identifiable persons and of their reactions to the conversations (whether they were annoyed, impatient or humorous).

Besides the silent daylight impressions, spoken daylight impressions were received by Mrs. Willett. She received these spoken messages when she was in a dreamlike state of trance. Mrs. Willett did sometimes enter a deep trancelike state, but even then she never lost possession of her body, that is, she never became ostensibly possessed. In this point she never reacted like an ordinary medium, who usually becomes ostensibly possessed, and loses control of her own body. In Mrs. Willett's state of apparent deep trance she would sit up and talk in a normal manner, though afterward she would remember little of what had transpired. In this phase Mrs.

Willett could talk or produce automatic writing and had visual or auditory experiences which were imaginal and not sensory, arising, as it were, outside her body.

For example, during sittings in which the late Professor Butcher was the ostensible communicator, Mrs. Willett experienced an hallucinatory smell of roses, which was quite meaningless to her. But the smell of roses had a definite association with certain of Professor Butcher's experiences during his lifetime. These were well known to the sitter. I personally know a woman who is not a developed medium, but who also experiences various types of hallucinatory olfaction (perfumes).

Mechanism of Mediumship

Telepathic mediumship. The communicator-persona, who are the object of Dr. Broad's investigations, maintain that it is only through the medium's awareness of them that they can become fully aware of themselves. That is, the reality of their being (of the communicator-persona) is dependent upon the communicator-persona being real to the medium. Thus, a communicator-persona is dependent on the medium for much of his "personality." In telepathic mediumship their thoughts are reportedly conveyed telepathically first to the medium, who then clothes them in the appropriate tactile, visual and kinesthetic imagery. Thus Mrs. Willett received the thoughts of the communicator-persona telepathically, whereupon she then expressed them in the normal way through her motor organs.

Telergic mediumship. The mechanism of ordinary mediumistic possession is apparently quite different to the above. Here the thoughts of the ostensible controlling persona are not received telepathically by the medium at all. For in this type of mediumship the medium's personality is directly ousted from the control of her sensory and motor organs. Her personality's place at the "console" which controls the instrumentation of the body is taken over by the communicator-persona until the medium comes out of her trance.

Thus, the communicator-persona in this case ostensibly thinks and expresses its own thoughts, employing the medium's nervous system via its "console" and effector organs to do so. An interesting point here is that the ostensible communicator-persona, if a man, can project a male voice, mannerisms, etc., via the female voice of the medium.

Summary. In summary, it seems that the communicator-persona can seize the controls of the medium's human body at apparently the same spot ("console") at which ordinary personality holds sway over the body. That is, somewhere within the body, probably in the nervous system, a control "console" in the body's instrumentation which is (in the case of certain susceptible persons such as mediums), susceptible of "takeover" by the persona under consideration. To use a political analogy: Just as revolutionaries are enabled to seize power when they take command of the radio, press, power installations, transport and parliament of a country, so a communicator-persona can seize control of a medium by ousting her own personality from the control "console" of her body. Presumably similar "takeovers" could also result from neural illness, stress, suggestion, etc.

The use of "relics" in mediumship. Mrs. Elliott's mediumship was investigated by Dr. Saltmarsh, particularly with respect to her successful use of relics (pieces of fingernail, skin, hair, letters or rings which had been connected with the dead person with whom the medium is to try to make contact) in her mediumistic activities.[13] Many other mediums and occultists use relics, of course, but the practice was investigated in Mrs. Elliott's case under particularly well-controlled conditions.

No theory was arrived at after completion of the investigations, which would explain the help which relics have been found to offer in facilitating mediumship of this type. But it is considered in some well-informed circles as fairly well proved that such relics do facilitate contact between the medium and the ostensible departed spirit with whom the relic was associated. On another plane, it is well known that modern witch doctors are delighted if they can obtain a lock of hair, a piece of fingernail or skin belonging to the person they wish to bring under their spells.

Dr. Broad describes Dr. Saltmarsh's carefully conceived and executed experiments. Relics were placed in sealed envelopes or packages and numbered with a code system known only to the experimenter. Pseudorelics, which had nothing to do with the "owner," were also used. To render the control more realistic, the pseudorelics usually belonged to someone who had been lost or who had died under similar circumstances to those surrounding the genuine person with whom contact was sought among the dead. The present owner of the relic might be present or absent during the sitting, which fact was carefully noted during the analysis of the results and scores. Sometimes Mrs. Elliott opened the envelope or packet and sometimes she did not. Whether or not she opened the envelope or packet containing the relic did not appear to influence the statistical results of the analysis. In one case relics from an ostensible communicator, who claimed to be an airman killed in action, were used together with relics from six pseudoowners, all of whom had lost a son or brother of about the same age as the ostensible communicator under similar circumstances. The total score reflecting the accuracy of Mrs. Elliott's communications using genuine relics amounted to 4,107. The total aggregate score calculated on the same basis but using pseudoowners of relics was 452. The maximal possible score under the scheme devised by Dr. Saltmarsh was 5,642. Thus the score on information using genuine relics from the real owner was 72.8 percent and that using relics belonging to pseudoowners (that is, fake relics), was 8 percent. For full details of this impressive and interesting experiment with true and false relics the reader is referred to Dr. Broad's detailed account.[14] There is no theory to date which explains the success of the medium in ostensibly contacting the dead person to whom the relic belonged or with whom it was closely associated.

Equally difficult to explain is the medium's lack of success, when, unknown to her, a pseudorelic was used.

Conclusions (mediumship and hallucinations). Dr. Broad comes to the conclusion that, in experiments with mediums such as those described, an enormous amount of padding and "high fallutin' twaddle"[15] surrounds the real information; but that, in spite of this padding and nonsense ("groping"), occasional gems of real information and coherent messages do emerge though they could not possibly have been known to the medium by normal means. Dr. Broad thinks that the best way to explain these facts is to postulate that this transfer of information is in the nature of a "leakage" or "seepage" from the foreign mind to the medium. The foreign mind seems to be able, for a short time, to determine what selected ideas occur in the medium's mind.

[1] C.E.M. Hansel, *ESP, A Scientific Evaluation.*
[2] C.D. Broad, *Lectures on Psychical Research.*
[3] *Ibid.,* pp. 113-52.
[4] *Ibid.,* p. 125.
[5] *Ibid.,* pp. 132-35.
[6] *Ibid.,* p. 137; cf. *Society for Psychical Research Proceedings,* 36: 517 ff.
[7] Broad, p. 139.
[8] *Ibid.,* p. 147.
[9] II Cor. 12.
[10] Broad, p. 169; cf. *Society for . . . ,* 39: 692.
[11] Broad, pp. 253-383.
[12] *Ibid.,* p. 257.
[13] *Ibid.,* pp. 315-33.
[14] *Ibid.,* p. 318.
[15] *Ibid.*

10. Psychical Structure
of the Human Individual

There is no need here for a discussion of the purely physical structure of the human brain—any textbook of physiology, neurology, anatomy or zoology will suffice. The structure of the mind, being less easily explored by present methods of research, is less well known although it has been and is being intensively studied.

One Personality Not Absolute

In the first place, some authorities years ago were inclined to regard the rule "one body, one ego or personality" as absolute. Ostensible possession shows that this view is certainly no longer tenable, for one ego can be ousted for a time from the control of a physical body, which is then taken charge of by another ostensibly different psychical being. This ousting of one personality by another happens regularly with trance mediums and apparently may also happen pathologically. The Holy Scriptures often report cases of both kinds, such as demon possession of men and animals. In addition to such cases, there are well-attested reports in medical literature of several "personalities" alternating in the control of one physical body.[1] Usually one personality is more developed than the others in its control of the one body, and the controlling personalities alternate with one another.

The condition in which several bodies are controlled by one personality or mind is more difficult to conceive of. One personality might occupy and control different bodies at different times, for example. However, a Lapplander, with his distinctive personality and dress could scarcely possess the same personality which animates an Australian aboriginal or a London professor of biochemistry. One personality could hardly share such widely differing bodies.

Dissecting of the Nature

The present problem therefore resolves itself into the unraveling or dissecting of the nature of the psychical individuality which animates a person's body during life and which leaves it at death. Most authorities agree that the ante-mortem human mind consists of at least two parts—the conscious and the subconscious. Various mediums have been questioned on matters concerning the structure of the human mind, and the communicator-persona have given varying answers. Most agree on the question of conscious and subconscious divisions. Mrs. Willett's communicators maintain, however, that there is a third division which they call the "transcendental" part. Others say little about this transcendental component. According to the communicators, at death there is an apparent shift in the dividing line between the conscious and the unconscious in the individual during life. Some communicators go so far as to maintain that, after death, the subconscious becomes fully concious, but that the old dividing line between the two divisions is reinstated when possession is taken of the medium's body. No cautious researcher would wish to be dogmatic here, for the evidence is conflicting and fragmentary.

Post-mortem Sense Organs

The Leonard communicators maintain that they possess post-mortem (after leaving the body) sense organs by means of which they perceive. They state, however, that they can and do use the medium's sense organs when in possession of her body. They even prefer to use the medium's eyes and ears in order to receive ordinary physical impressions when in possession. On the other hand, they maintain that they use their own auditory sense organs for hearing the voices of communicators.

This brings us to the question of the psychical structure of the alleged communicators as psychical beings. They obviously hold an animistic view of themselves and of human beings, which is today very outdated in intellectual circles. Nevertheless, out of date or not, these communicators are apparently immune to the dictates of fashion in scientific work and teach the existence of an "astral" body, which is supramaterial, and therefore not compatible with ordinary human sense perception during physical life. The mind allegedly "informs" the astral body and is indissolubly united to it to form a human "soul." Thus, before death, a human being consists of a physical body united to a soul which is in its turn indissolubly united to an "astral body." The soul and the astral body animate the material body. Thus, in a way, the human is looked upon by these communicators as a trinity. At death the astral body and the soul (mind) leave the physical body, which then decays.

Dr. Broad points out that the evidence for these things is good but that modern materialistic and psychical science have simply swamped the evidence and, therefore, the theories, out of widespread acceptance today.[2]

CARTESIAN VIEWS AND SWEDENBORG

Mental Substance or Thought

Opposed to these animistic views proposing a mind, a physical and astral body in life and an astral body and mind post-mortem, are the Cartesian views. Proponents of these views propose, instead of an astral body and a mind post-mortem, a purely mental substance or thought (with no astral body) which exists after death. Thus, pure thought or mental substance is united with the body ante-mortem but persists without a body, psychic or otherwise, after death.

Swedenborg, before he went through his experience with departed spirits, accepted the Cartesian views on human structure, and believed that if men survive physical death, they do so as pure disembodied minds or pure thought unassociated with psychical or astral bodies. However, during Swedenborg's experiences with the spirits of the dead, he allegedly met both spirits who held the Cartesian views and those who held the animistic views. Some spirits believed themselves to be pure mental substance, while others, actually in the majority, found themselves to have sense perception and believed therefore (even after they had been dead for some time) that they were not dead and possessed ordinary bodies.

Scriptural Support

Today, these views, if held at all, are regarded as evidence that the holder is a crackpot—and Dr. Broad says so, eminent philosopher and psychical research worker that he is. But surely it is unwise to reject an hypothesis on such a basis. Swedenborg, apart from his meetings with the spirits, was an eminently intelligent and learned man who looked after his wordly affairs in a sane and efficient manner. The same remarks apply to the often learned men who wrote the Old Testament and the New Testament and who also believed in survival in both the embodied and disembodied state after death. Indeed, they apply to our Lord himself, for the Scriptures report his similar views on the reality of the post-mortem life and the continuing individuality of the spirits in that state.

The Old Testament, in which Christ implicitly believed, reports one case in which the alleged communicator from the dead was the Prophet Samuel, who was brought up from the realms of the dead by the woman at Endor who possessed a "familiar spirit." That is, she was a medium who had been, incidentally, one of many mediums before Saul, the king who now consulted her, had murdered them.[3] Mediumship is thus a very old profession, and dealt then, as now, with the reality and continuing identity of the dead. In a similar vein the Scriptures report that Christ preached to the spirits of the dead.[4]

The Scriptures go even further in the direction reported on today by psychical researchers, for they describe what was surely a spectacular experience in the life of the Apostle Paul.[5] Modern psychical researchers would describe the Apostle Paul's as an "out of the body" experience. For the apostle says explicitly that during this experience and afterward he did not know whether he was in the body or out of it.[6] But he did hear "unspeakable words, which it is not lawful for a man to utter." He gives a general impression of the experience, however, by saying he was "caught up to the third heaven" and "caught up into paradise." Less prominent persons than the great apostle have had similar experiences which cannot be explained away by mere scoffing.

Ability to Communicate

Further, Swedenborg has some interesting information on the ability of psychical beings to communicate. He says that they are in a position to ransack the innermost memories of dead and living persons, and maintains that it was just this facility which accounted for the power of spirits to imitate and impersonate Swedenborg's friends.

The alleged mode of communication is not ordinary human language but a system of visual images and pictorial ideas conveyed back and forth telepathically. The human receiving these images automatically translates them into his own everyday language. Swedenborg maintains that this explains a fact which had mystified him for a long time, namely, that the spirits of foreigners usually spoke to him in Swedish. Even spirits reputedly long dead, whose death took place before modern Swedish had arisen, spoke to him in impeccable modern Swedish! This might throw light on the gift of tongues conferred by the Holy Spirit at Pentecost.[7] May not the mechanism of this gift from God have been something similar? The images received from the apostles' lips may have been automatically decoded into the language normally used by the hearer, even though the latter did not understand the actual image transmitted to him.

Swedenborg maintained that the spirits of the recently dead go through the motions of communication with each other by speech. This is allegedly due to the illusion under which they labor, imagining that they are still in possession of a physical body. Later the spirits communicate only by visual telepathy.

THE THEORETICAL SIGNIFICANCE OF DREAMS AND SURVIVAL AFTER DEATH

Vivid and Sustained Sensations

Although the tendency of most educated (and uneducated) people today is to reject, out of hand, any and all evidence for the supranormal and for psychical survival (insofar as pure physical science cannot account for such evidence), yet we possess in ourselves evidence which, as Dr. Broad puts it,[8] should warn us to consider the subject carefully before we reject the evidence too rashly. For the mechanisms by which we regularly and normally produce dreams show that we can experience vivid and sustained sensations which arise apart from purely physical sense perception. In a nightmare we can dream and experience the lion springing on us and feel the excruciating pain of his taking a chunk out of the muscles of our right arm. In reality a mosquito may have bitten us, or by lying too long in one position we have cut off the blood supply, or our dream may have had no physical basis at all. But there was no adequate physical stimulation to correspond to the "experience" of a "real" attack by a lion. Dr. Broad's conclusion[9] is that this fact may be relevant to the possibility of psychic survival. Since ordinary human beings can think thoughts not based on material physical stimulation, is it not conceivable that if a person survived the death of his physical body, he might carry with him the mechanism and materials for producing such internally coherent phantasmagoria without needing external stimulation? If so, he might continue, even though disembodied, to live, as it were, in a kind of dream world not so very unlike the world which he actually inhabited when embodied. (Though Dr. Broad is never certain himself that there will be survival after death, and believes it unlikely that most human beings will survive death.)

Structure of Human Entity

Concerning the actual structure of that part of the human entity which might survive death, Dr. Broad is exceedingly cautious.[10] He points out that in past history few have believed in a disembodied survival in the Cartesian sense. Buddhists and Hindus believe in survival by reincarnation, either in another human, or in an animal, or in the nonphysical body of a god. But in these beliefs in survival some sort of body always figures. Christians, on the other hand, believe in the biblical concept of a kind of disembodied survival up to the general resurrection, at which time a supernatural resurrection body is assumed by the dead. This new body is similar, according to perfectly clear scriptural statements, to the visible, tangible yet supramaterial body which Christ received after his resurrection.[11] This body was capable of eating fish and making a fire as well as of talking and looking exactly like a normal physical body.[12] Yet, it could instantly vanish while the disciples were looking at him. That is, Christians believe that the material body is somehow related to (and bound up in) a supramaterial body and that each redeemed person will receive at resurrection such a supramaterial body which Christ is preparing for him while he spends his life in the purely material body.

Belief of Philosophers

Philosophers such as Spinoza and countless others believed in human immortality of some sort, so that it betrays shallow thought and perhaps intellectual arrogance to maintain that only the credulous and ignorant believe what these eminent intellectuals believed. Dr. Broad says on the same subject:

> If survival be conceivable, then I cannot but think that the least implausible form of the hypothesis would be that, at any rate immediately after death and for some indefinite period later, the surviving personality is embodied in some kind of non-physical body, which was during life associated in some intimate way with the physical body.[13]

Later Dr. Broad adds:

> The doctrine of reincarnation [is] . . . at any rate one conceivable form of human survival . . . of sufficient theoretical interest and *prima facie* plausibility to deserve considerably more attention from psychical researchers . . . than it has hitherto received.[14]

The ψ-Component

Referring to the hypothetical psychical part of a human which is presumably united to his physical body, Dr. Broad designates it as the "ψ-component." It will obviously carry some of the marks of individual personality and is modified more or less permanently during its life experiences when combined with the body. Exactly how this ψ-component is united to the physical body and how ostensible communicators take possession of a medium's body are unknown today. But Dr. Broad likens the psychical persistence of a human to the persistence of the radio transmission of an orchestral piece in a region where no tuned receiver (body) exists.[15] Without a tuned receiver no one could maintain that there was evidence for the orchestral piece in the area concerned. And they would be perfectly correct as far as sound waves, to which their ears are sensitive, are involved.

The medium might be considered to play the part of the tuned radio in this case.

Thus, Dr. Broad concludes that this form of dualism, this combination between a ψ-component and a physical body, one tuned to or combined with the other, is not inconsistent with the known laws of physics, physiology or psychology. On the other hand, Dr. Broad boldly states that, apart from some of the psychical phenomena which he has reported on, there is *nothing whatsoever* in the physical sciences to support this dualistic view of human structure. He adds that, if he, like most contemporary philosophers and scientists in the West, were frankly ignorant of (or blandly indifferent to) the psychical phenomena we have partially described, his own views would be those of a materialistic Westerner. Dr. Broad's perplexing difficulty is that he is *not* ignorant of nor blandly indifferent to the psychical facts, and is therefore not content to "emulate the ostrich."[16]

Human Makeup of ψ-Component

On this basis Dr. Broad and his collaborators believe firmly in the existence in the human makeup of a ψ-component which is postulated to be discarnate when not associated with the brain or nervous system in our human bodies. This ψ-component he regards as a complex vortex in an "old-fashioned ether."[17] It is considered to be a kind of "field" associated with the living brain and nervous system and with the events taking place in them. However, unlike a field, it can exist as a vortex without being associated with the physical nervous system or brain.

Since this proposed ψ-component would be at least partially deprived of sensory impulses after being parted from the body previously associated with it, it would presumably go into a state of rest (or sleep) after parting in death from its physical body, in the same way in which a living human goes to sleep on being cut off from sensory impulses when he lies in a quiet room at night. If this ψ-component at a later date received back a transcendental body, the "rest" or "sleep" of the disembodied ψ-component would then be broken by new impulses coming in from the new "body," and a "resurrection" would have thereby taken place. The evangelical Christian does not believe in "soul sleep," but he does believe that at death the Christian rests from his works and waits for the resurrection morning, when soul and resurrection body will be joined, prior to the ecstasy of the "resurrection day" in the presence of Christ.

Basis of Physical Attributes

We will conclude this consideration of Dr. Broad's views by commenting on one further point of his postulated ψ-component. If the ψ-component is related in some way to communicator persona in mediumship, then the ψ-component must carry with it the basis of some highly characteristic, apparently physical attributes. For the communicator-persona is able to modify in a decisive manner the handwriting, voice and other physical characteristics of the medium during alleged possession. For during automatic handwriting the style is not that of the medium but that of the alleged communicator. Similarly, the tone of voice during a trance session in which alleged possession takes place, may not be the female voice of the medium, but that of a child or a man. The same applies to various mannerisms, which are not those of the medium, but belong to the ostensible communicator. The ψ-component is thus considered to be in some way the carrier of these and other attributes which are imposed on the medium's body.

To explain these observations Dr. Broad compares the body of a medium to an unsaturated organic compound which is able to attract and bind several ψ-components. The ordinary person's body binds just one ψ-component for life. The medium's body temporarily assumes the attributes of another ψ-component. But, says Dr. Broad, these phenomena are by no means general. In fact they are, today at least, rare. For in general it is still true that "dead men tell no tales." Dr. Broad is of the opinion that in the normal and abnormal phenomena of life there is nothing to suggest survival after death.

He holds that "straightforward survival of the personality of a deceased human being is antecedently the least likely of all alternatives under discussion."[18] Here, as throughout his works, Dr. Broad does not regard the Bible as authoritative in these or any other matters, though he often refers to the Scriptures to make a point.

Christ's Resurrection

Our factual (as opposed to revelationary) evidence for survival after death rests squarely on the well-attested paranormal phenomena we have been describing. To these we may add the vastly superior and much better attested phenomena connected with the resurrection of Christ. Both phenomena offer coercive evidence for individual survival and throw light on the transcendental makeup of the normal human being.

If survival after death represents the survival of a non-material component of the human organism after separation from a purely material component, this is exactly the state of affairs we would expect. That is, under these conditions we would expect no normal or even abnormal evidence for such survival. Dr. Broad points out that there is no normal or abnormal evidence for such survival, but *paranormal* evidence might be expected and looked for, and it is just such evidence for survival which Dr. Broad notes.

The reason for this state of affairs is that if the physical component of the human structure is strictly three-dimensional and if survival represents the continuation of a component which is supra-three-dimensional, then any evidence for survival which is supra-three-dimensional may not be perceivable as such in a purely three-dimensional "physical-scientific" setting. Obviously, if the surviving element of the human after death is not physical (or is purely supra-physical) then merely physical evidence could not be expected to betray such nonphysical survival. Only paranormal evidence is going to reveal the paranormal survival of a paranormal component. I have treated this matter at length in another publication.[19]

OTHER VIEWS ON MAN'S PSYCHICAL STRUCTURE

Artificial Consciousness and Intelligence

There are, of course, other views on the structure of the human psyche than the one we have described above. Bergson's and Broad's views certainly do not exercise a monopoly in present-day speculation on man's inner makeup.

Alternative theories to those here described believe, in some cases, that the brain in physically so constructed that it can produce endogenously all the intelligence and consciousness which are properties observable scientifically.

James T. Culbertson believes, for example, that it is today completely possible to "describe a general method for designing robots with *any* specified behavioral properties whatsoever. They can be designed to do any desired physically possible thing under any given circumstances and past experience, and certainly any naturally given 'robot,' such as Smith or Jones, can do no more. Remember, of course, that we are assuming—quite contrary to fact—that all the neurons we want are available, that they are small enough, etc., and that we have enough mechanical dexterity and time to assemble them. Since we make these assumptions we hereinafter disregard such practical difficulties."[20]

Culbertson believes that it is theoretically possible to construct three main types of robot today—those with no memories, those with complete memories, and those with selective memories like our own. If the complete specifications can be given, any species of robot is theoretically possible today, even though not necessarily practicable. Complete robots would be fantastically complicated and uneconomical in design. However, theoretically speaking, they could show, as a special case, entirely human behavior.[21]

Culbertson asks his readers the following practical question:

> How can we design automata with the complexity of, say, human beings and yet do it with no more cells than are in the human brain? In the sequel, we claim that this can be done by making the automata conscious. . . . Our interest shifts entirely from the behavioral problem to the problem of consciousness (for its own sake); i.e. how to design the automata so that they will experience sense data regardless of what behavior results. . . . Conscious automata are more economical than unconscious automata when the behavior required is sufficiently complex. . . . In principle, robots simulating human behavior could be designed. The analysis of the complete robot makes it perfectly clear, however, that *practical* difficulties definitely preclude the use of this type of design for the construction of artificial human beings.[22]

Complete robots, while theoretically possible, would require too many central cells. A general robot with only forty receptors would require more than 10^{10} neurons. The brain size and weight would be too large to be practicable. A main purpose of Culbertson's argument is that, even though these designs for robots, using transistors or tubes in the place of biological neurons, are far too cumbersome to be practicable, yet by means of these artificial neurons the same end results in behavior and consciousness can be achieved as biological neurons achieve in man and animals. The conclusion is therefore drawn that consciousness is not something specially limited to biological life but is electrically produceable by other means which we have at our disposal now. Thus Culbertson and others believe that artificial intelligence will be attainable in the not too distant future. If this is really the case, then we shall be able to talk and reason with a complete robot in exactly the same way as we can with a human. By extrapolation, superhuman intelligence could be developed in robots to run the world better than human beings can—they could do better research and development work and put mankind out of work requiring intelligence.

Culbertson believes that the use of transistors and tubes as artificial neurons in the development of artificial intelligence can be compared with the use of propellers in artificial flight instead of wings and feathers.[23] The bird achieves the end of flight with muscles and feathers, while the plane achieves the same end by means of jet engines and propellers. But the principles of flight (and thought and consciousness) remain the same in both cases.

Pertinent Questions

Even though the development of artificial complete electronic androids lies in the future we can nevertheless ask ourselves a number of questions pertinent to the nature of man psychically speaking. If an android capable of every kind of human behavior were produced, would that fact prove that man and his entire mind are entirely material in structure? That is, does man possess, all the same, a transcendental part?

Granted that a complete android could be produced which could produce the equivalent in intellectual work (or better) that we can produce, would that prove that man is entirely material? There would be one way of proving such a question to the satisfaction of scientists such as Broad and Bergson. We would have to test androids of the type in view for paranormal phenomena such as biological man does, at times, show. Ostensible possession, ESP of the type we have attempted to describe, as well as out-of-the-body experiences, would all require demonstration in the android before one could maintain that it was entirely equivalent in structure to man. For such phenomena are the *only proof* we have for believing that man does contain a transcendental part in his being. While the major portion of man's consciousness, intelligence, personality and psyche may be resident in his physiological brain and dependent on a good supply of oxygenated haemoglobin, there are some functions of man's personality which are not. The question is, therefore, whether a synthetic complete android would show the paranormal behavior that some human beings are known to show. If not, the android could be said to be entirely material while the human was not.

We have introduced this recent development in the field of robots to demonstrate the importance of Bergson's, Broad's and Huxley's views over against the purely material views of man which are tending to prevail today. The experiment to establish whether an android could be transcendent in the same way that a biological human can be regarded as transcendent, cannot yet be carried out. But the possibility of such developments must be clearly borne in mind in these days of rapid development in the field of artificial intelligence. No one today is in the position to state dogmatically that *all* the attributes of all human beings can be accounted for on an entirely materialistic basis. We therefore shall continue to assume that the human psyche may be connected by a "reduction valve" to Mind-at-Large, in order to account for some of his psychical attributes.

THE CONNECTION BETWEEN PSYCHICAL PHENOMENA AND HALLUCINATORY DRUGS

Using the above evidence on the physical and psychical structure of the human, it becomes feasible to propose some mechanisms by which hallucinatory drugs may produce their effects.

Leakage or Seepage of Thought

As already suggested, the phenomenon of telepathy may indicate a leakage or seepage of thought from one mind to another, or to and from Mind-at-Large. If the seepage is weak, obviously the strong sensory and proprioceptive impulses occurring as a result of modern Western civilization will tend to swamp any recognition of this seepage, so that modern, hasty, busy, noisy man will sincerely and totally deny its existence.

But under the influence of LSD even modern man may experience such strong inhibition or alteration of sensory and proprioceptive impulses across his neural synapses that the ratio of seepage impulses to ordinary neural impulses is altered. He may thus recognize the seepage for the first time—as long as he is under the drug influence. Of course, he may explain the hallucinatory action on the basis that it arises as a result of internal self-activity of the brain. That is, that within itself the brain generates the hallucinations under drug influence.

Is drug hallucination self-generated? On the basis of purely physical science I do not think that we are yet in a position to decide whether all drug hallucination is self-generated or not. There is, however, good evidence that some drug hallucination resembles some sensory-deprivation hallucination, so that the two may be similar and not necessarily due to a pathological functioning of the brain. Even pathological hallucination, such as occurs in schizophrenia, has points in common with drug and sensory-deprivation hallucination, so that hallucination would seem to be a general phenomenon (like dreaming), which is triggered by varied causes.

Increase of sensory impulses. The problem of deciding whether drug or sensory deprivation hallucination is self-generated or not, may be illuminated by the following: The strength of sensory impulses reaching the decoding centers of the average Western individual's brain today must have vastly increased along with the pace of mechanized modern life and communications, compared with the kind of signals which reached the same centers in our ancestors. Parallel with the increase of sensory impulses, mystical, transcendent and even ordinary religious experience has sharply decreased with the development of modern life everywhere. That is, the busier and noisier man has become, the less mystical and religious he is. In general, secularization leads to minimal religious experience. This picture is true wherever one looks in the world today. It applies to the secularization of Japan, as well as in the South Sea Islands, Lapland or Spain. The old religions and transcendental beliefs of the peoples of the whole earth are melting away in the face of the noise, bustle, secularization and materialism of modern civilization.

Seepage becomes swamped. This observation fits in with the hypothesis which we have discussed—that at least some hallucination may be a result of seepage into the mind from Mind outside. This seepage becomes swamped by the adventitious mass of neural "noise" and sensory impulses arising from modern life. This is only another way of restating the scriptural teaching that the cares or overactivity of this life make a man deaf to the transcendental realities surrounding him.[24] In confirming the relevance of this teaching it should be remembered that even an LSD adept can often obtain no satisfactory trip unless he is left either alone, in the quiet presence of others engaged in the same activity, or with his psychiatrist. Even the nervous activity produced by other people coming and going during a therapeutic LSD trip is often sufficient to weaken the hallucinatory impressions from which the patient might have benefited.

Increasing Nervous System Capacity

Hallucinatory drugs may function by increasing the capacity of the nervous system for combination with the ψ-component—or even with Mind-at-Large. To use Dr. Broad's analogy, the relative "unsaturation" of the nervous system for the ψ-component (or Mind-at-Large) may be increased under the use of hallucinatory drugs, thus increasing perception of the transcendental.

Loosen "Combination Strength"

On the other hand, hallucinatory drugs may *loosen* the "combination strength" ("bond strength") between normal individual systems and their ψ-components, rendering the individuals "unstable" psychically. Thus the "compound" between ψ-components and their physical nervous system becomes more "labile" under hallucinatory drug influence. Ostensible possession (or "recombination") between the living nervous system and other ψ-components would then be more liable to occur. This merely means that "dissociation" of ψ-components and physical nervous systems could occur more easily, with resultant psychical instability. This might fit into the neurosis- and psychosis-producing effect of LSD in certain individuals.

On the basis of modern psychical research these questions cannot be resolved at present. The important point to notice, however, is that even though psychical research has not advanced very far, its general progress has neither outdated nor negated the scriptural position, especially in psychical matters. This applies to the positive survival of good and bad individuals after death to receive the fruits of their ante-mortem acts. It also applies to what Dr. Broad calls the ψ-component, which is supposed to combine with the physical brain in animating a body. After death this "vortex in an old-fashioned ether" is said by the Scriptures to return to God, who gave it.[25]

DANGERS OF PRACTICING OR INVESTIGATING MEDIUMSHIP AND SPIRITISM

Strong Warnings in Scripture

The practice of mediumship and the investigation into its mysteries are not without their dangers. Even skeptical psychical research workers such as Dr. C. D. Broad acknowledge this fact. But the warnings which such serious workers as Dr. Broad utter are mild compared with those found throughout Holy Scripture on this subject.

The history of the Jews from earliest times is characterized by their tendency to turn to mediums for help whenever they became apostate from God. At the beginning of the reign of their first king, Saul, the land was well supplied with women who had "familiar spirits," or were mediums. In his earlier and more zealous years Saul ferreted out these women and either banished them or had them executed. This activity was an attempt to obey Jehovah's commands against such practices. But after he had himself become an apostate, when as a result of his disobedience the Lord no longer answered his petitions, Saul turned to the woman at Endor who had contact with the dead through her familiar spirit, through whom she brought up Samuel from the dead during a nocturnal séance. From the account given of the affair in I Samuel 28, it appears from the shriek uttered by the medium when Samuel appeared that she was thoroughly shocked, and recognized Saul at once, although he was disguised. The solemnity of the séance was added to when Samuel, from the regions of the dead, confirmed the word of God which he had spoken while he was alive, "The LORD has done to you as he spoke by me."[26] Samuel still retained in the state of death his prophetic and visionary gift, for he also saw God taking Saul and his sons the very next day in death. "Tomorrow you and your sons shall be with me," that is, in the state of death. Samuel's spirit also retained in death the memory of what he had done and said during his lifetime as a prophet.

Thus, the awesome shade of Samuel, with the aid of the medium, was able to remonstrate with Saul for his apostate state, to confirm the infallibility of God's prophetic word as well as to prophesy what would and did happen the very next day. For the next day Saul fell upon his own sword in fear of losing the battle against the Philistines. His sons also fell. Yet Samuel's brain was physiologically long since dead.

Many Christians make light of this séance. If the spirit who spoke with Saul was a lying demon, is it likely that he would confirm God's word out of hand and be able to prophesy accurately the plan God had for Saul and his sons the next day? Personally, although I am sure there is a great deal of fraud in modern mediumship, I believe that this very counterfeit proves the reality of a small but genuine number of mediums who practice necromancy or traffic with the dead.

Mediumship Is Apostasy

But the sobering fact is that this case of mediumship at Endor, which is described in such detail in the Scripture, is intended to show us the depth and gravity of the apostasy into which King Saul and his followers fell. That is, mediumship, in the eyes of the God of Holy Scripture, is a symptom of a serious form of apostasy from the living God. Nor is this reference to mediumship the only one in the Holy Scriptures. In fact, mediumship is classed with the "abominable practices" of the heathen which the Jews were commanded not to imitate:

> When you come into the land which the LORD your God gives you, you shall not learn to follow the abominable practices of those nations. There shall not be found among you any one who burns his son or daughter as an offering, any one who practices divination, a soothsayer, or an augur, or a sorcerer, or a charmer, or a *medium*, or a wizard, or a *necromancer. For whoever does these things is an abomination to the Lord; and because of these abominable practices the Lord your God is driving them out before you.*[27]

Thus, mediumship is classed in Scripture with the sacrifice of human burnt offerings. Other scriptures warn: "Do not turn to *mediums* or wizards; *do not seek them out,* to be defiled by them: I am the LORD your God."[28] "A man or a woman who is a *medium* or a wizard shall be put to death."[29] "So do not listen to your prophets, your diviners, your dreamers, your soothsayers, or your sorcerers, who are saying to you, 'You shall not serve the king of Babylon.' "[30]

The warnings of the Old Testament against mediums or those possessing familiar spirits (Hebrew, *ob*), also known as necromancers, are very numerous, as reference to any good concordance will rapidly show.

New Testament Cases

In the New Testament, Luke, in the Acts of the Apostles, reports cases of the practice of occult arts (Acts 8:9 describes the case of Simon, a sorcerer who practiced magic and who resisted the gospel. And Acts 13:6-11 gives the account of Elymas, a magician who also resisted the gospel and was blinded for a time for this resistance). But the New Testament also speaks a good deal of what appears to be overt demon possession.

In Acts 8:7 we find unclean spirits leaving many of the possessed and crying out with a loud voice as they did so. Acts 16:16 tells of the slave girl who had a "spirit of divination" and earned good money for her owners in this capacity. The Apostle Paul charged the spirit to come out of her, and it left her "that very hour," much to the chagrin of her owners. Acts 19 reports how evil spirits were cast out on a large scale. Matthew 8:28-32 depicts how the Lord cast out the demons from two demoniacs, whereupon the demons entered and destroyed a herd of swine.

Barrier Not to Be Bridged

So God, in both the Old and New Testaments, regards mediumship or other traffic with the spirits of the dead as a very serious offense against his laws. *He has set a barrier between the living and the dead which is, in our age and dispensation, not intended to be bridged.* The reason for this gulf between the dead and the living may be that the spirits of the dead might be able to impersonate other spirits, thus opening the way to many forms of deceit and fraud. Remember that Swedenborg maintained that spirits have the power of ransacking the minds of the living as well as the dead, thus almost interfering with the fixity of personality itself. If this sort of ransacking were possible on a general scale what chaos would follow in the realms of the living!

Drugs in Revelation

One interesting matter should be pointed out before we leave this aspect of our subject. The book of Revelation is the prime source in the Bible which specifically mentions sorcery or enchantment (which might approach what we call a "trip" under drug influence today) by means of drugs. Revelation 9:21 mentions *pharmakeia,* meaning enchantment by drugs (cf. also Rev. 18:23 where the same word is used). Revelation

21:8 mentions *pharmakeus,* meaning an enchanter who uses drugs. Revelation 22:15 refers to *pharmakos,* also meaning an enchanter by means of drugs (cf. Gal. 5:20). In all these cases the author of the Revelation rejects those who bring about enchantment by means of drugs and maintains that such sorcerers are outside the kingdom.

In view of the fact that the book of the Revelation is generally believed to be a prophecy referring to the time of the end of the age, these references to sorcery—or its modern equivalent (the changing of a person's mood, state of consciousness or will by means of drugs so that the subject is brought under the will of another) may be very important. For certain nations already use drugs to force their innocent subjects to confess to all types of crimes. In short, what may be envisaged here is the possible use of drugs for the "enchantment" or "spellbinding" of wide sections of the population in "the time of the end." Brainwashing by means of drugs, to use modern terminology, may be a subject to which Christians should give more serious attention. In any case, it is interesting that the Revelation should be the book in which these matters are mentioned.

SUPPLEMENTARY EVIDENCE

Experience of Composers

Great musicians such as Mozart, Bach, Beethoven, Handel and Mendelssohn are generally reputed not to have "made up" or "worked out" their music. Handel shut himself up without contact with the outside world and with little food or drink for weeks while he was transcribing the score of the "Messiah" as he "received" it. Neglecting everything else, he says, he "listened" to the composition and wrote down the masterpiece. The same thing is reported of Mozart. It is indeed so general a phenomenon that the word *Eingebung* (German, "something which is given to one from elsewhere") has been coined for it.[30a]

Under the influence of LSD and other hallucinatory drugs

at least one modern composer has "listened" to music from "other spheres" in drug trances, has remembered the music after the trance, and then written it down. This would bear out Dr. Broad's view of consciousness, with perhaps the addendum that musicians must have a less constricted "reducing valve" from their consciousness to a Mind-at-Large of musical consciousness! Many creative scientists, artists, thinkers and writers including Einstein, Poincaré, Cocteau, A. E. Housman, Nietzsche, Henry Moore and D. H. Lawrence confirm this phenomenon, in which they receive ideas or concepts or even specific phrases "whole," seemingly from an outside source.[31]

Sensory Deprivation and Hallucination

It is a fact, repeatedly verified in recent times, that some of the effects of hallucinatory drugs can be achieved without the aid of drugs. Deprivation of normal sensory impulses to the brain, for example, may cause hallucinations without drug aid.

Lack of food and water. Thus, hallucinations involving water or food may occur in those who are starving or dying of thirst, and are thus deprived of the normal stimulation of food or drink. It is perhaps significant, in this connection, that prayer and fasting in the biblical setting were often the prerequisite for dreams and certain forms of prophetic visions. The Apostle Peter had been fasting (i.e., undergoing sensory deprivation) when he saw the vision of the sheet let down from heaven with a variety of animals in it.[32] The Prophet Daniel experienced similar dreams and visions in connection with his fasts and prayers.[33] The Apostle Paul went down to the isolation of Arabia and there experienced his out-of-the-body experience.[34] One may justly classify these experiences as having taken place under the general heading of special sensory deprivation. It seems that such messages from God "got through" when extraneous cerebral "noise" was reduced by the deprivation.

Isolation from others. Space medicine, involving the

testing of human beings under conditions of lengthy isolation from contact with other humans in their space capsules, has turned up an interesting related phenomenon. Astronauts thus isolated in simulated space flights have reported experiencing hallucinatory effects which in some cases threatened to interfere with the efficient carrying out of their scientific work during space-capsule experiments. Students, confined in dark, acoustically insulated rooms for long periods, have been reported as showing hallucinatory behavior which was rapidly corrected when they were restored to their normal social environment.

This phenomenon is now well known and is designated as sensory-deprivation hallucination. Its symptoms simulate those of certain hallucinatory drugs. On the basis of Dr. Broad's theories, the parallels between hallucinatory drug phenomena and those produced by sensory deprivation may be explained partially on the following basis:

Overloading of brain. It is well known that perceptive overloading of the brain can cause general or local anesthesia. An experiment carried out some years ago demonstrated this fact conclusively. A tooth was painlessly extracted from a patient without the use of local or general anesthetics by the simple expedient of supplying him with a pair of earphones into which music or "white noise" was piped. A volume control device was given to the patient so that he could vary the volume of sound in the headphones. As the surgical manipulations began to cause pain, the patient was instructed to step up the volume of the music or "white noise" to achieve stronger anesthesia.

The theory worked out in practice. The tooth was painlessly extracted. By applying sufficient sensory overloading through the ears, pain perception from other centers (teeth) was crowded out. The brain is capable of handling only a strictly limited sensory input from all five senses. When the auditory input via the ears was vastly increased by stepping up the volume in the headphones, there was no room left in the brain deciphering centers to analyze and decode messages from the dental pain receptors. Thus, on pulling the tooth, pain messages were sent to the brain from the insulted tissue area, but because all the "lines" in the brain "switchboard" were swamped with "heavy" messages from the ears, when the pain messages arrived they could not be handled. Therefore, no pain was felt, even though no local anesthetic was used.

Soldiers injured in battle. The same sort of phenomenon has often been noted by soldiers in the thick of battle where the individual soldier's brain was overloaded with the millions of impulses necessary for survival and military response. Men in battle have been seriously wounded without even noticing it. Feet, ears and other members have been mutilated or shot off in the heat of battle, but the soldier has carried on, because there were no "lines" in the brain "switchboard" free to decode the pain messages reaching the brain from the traumatized tissues. Only after the fighting is over do these soldiers begin to feel the pain of their wounds. The "lines" become less busy, the centers for decoding and handling pain impulses become less overloaded, with the result that pain messages get through, and the soldier becomes aware of his wounds—there all the time, but unfelt, and their pain messages undecoded.

Everyday experience in the summer shows that sunburn often does not hurt much during activity of the day, but at night, when everything is quiet, the pain can become intolerable. The pain was there all the time, even during the day, but the pain impulses became felt more strongly as the proportion of other sensory impulses to pain impulses decreased at night.

Result of drug influence. If, now, the brain is connected by a "reducing valve" to Mind-at-Large, and if this valve becomes less "watertight" and the proprioceptive synapses partly blocked under the influence of hallucinatory drugs, then more message impulses from Mind-at-Large may penetrate in spite of the valve. The messages may be distorted, as hallucinations often are, by the passage through the valve "constriction." Nevertheless, more impulses could seep through under drug influence. The seepage signal strength may be weak or strong according to the drug used and according to the constitution of the patient concerned.

Factors determining reception. The important point is that the actual *registration* and *deciphering* of the messages from Mind-at-Large will, however, obviously be *dependent* on two factors: the signal strength of the rest of the impulses reaching the brain centers from the proprioceptors of the whole body, and the signal strength seeping through the "restriction valve."

Thus, a loud noise propagated by the proprioceptors may profoundly influence an LSD experience, simply because the noise impulse competes for deciphering centers in the brain with the comparatively weak signals from Mind-at-Large. If the signal from Mind-at-Large is weak and the noise signals loud, the former may be entirely swamped by the latter, so that no drug effect is registered and the hallucinations or drug experience are destroyed. This happens if persons come and go during an LSD experience. They may disturb the achievement of any useful experience at all when LSD is used therapeutically, as already mentioned. All extraneous sensory input must therefore be carefully regulated and reduced during the LSD experience.

The quiet social groups typical of marijuana smokers are probably conducive to reduction of normal brain sensory proprioceptive input, which would compete with the weak signal entering through the reducing valve under the influence of the drug. Thus the weak signal from Mind-at-Large is more promptly and carefully handled, and the drug effect increased when quiet conditions are maintained while using marijuana and similar drugs.

Space-capsule experience. Consider now the case of the normal individual not under the influence of drugs, but undergoing sensory deprivation in a space capsule. Individuals undergoing such experiences are usually chosen for their general good health, and normally speaking would not be subject to hallucinations. To use Henri Bergson's postulate once more, we would expect the reducing valves of such persons to be rather firmly closed so that only a minimal seepage could occur from Mind-at-Large. Normally the mind of such a person is so occupied with healthy deciphering and decoding of input from the proprioceptors—hearing, seeing, tasting, feeling and smelling—that the minute trickle through the valve to and from "regions beyond" goes entirely undecoded.

In our healthy astronaut normal brain traffic is ordinarily so heavy that it swamps completely any weak trickle via the reducing valve. Therefore he is never normally subject to "imaginations." But when he is cut off from the flood of normal healthy impulses entering his brain, he undergoes sensory deprivation. The lines are no longer so busy that they can ignore the trickle. The trickle through the reducing valve becomes, in fact, the mainstream of impulses entering the brain. For the first time, therefore, this trickle begins to be registered, with the result that our astronaut begins to become hallucinated. He begins to see and hear things which do not exist in our material three-dimensional world. His medical advisers thereupon pump in "normal" impulses, destroy his sensory deprivation and effectively swamp his hallucinations with normal sensory brain input. This is a reason why many people never hear the voice of eternity until they are cut off from the flood of impulses resulting from a busy life. It takes the death of a loved one, or illness, to establish this contact with eternity by interrupting a busy life.

It seems that drugs like LSD "enlarge" the reduction valve, thus increasing the signal strength (see p.   ) via the valve, which then by competition, forces the brain to recognize the signal and to decipher it, in spite of other normal competing traffic. Sensory deprivation seems to achieve the same effect by leaving the input "seepage" signal at the same strength, but at the same time reducing competing traffic. LSD increases the "seepage" and may at the same time under certain circumstances even slow down normal proprioception across the synapses, thus reducing competition. But in general, perception and awareness (consciousness) are *increased* under LSD and similar drugs, as well as hallucination. Thus both types of input may be stepped up.

Connection with Scripture. These theories, for they are no more than that, would seem to be connected with the emphasis placed by Holy Scripture on prayer, the quiet time and perhaps fasting, as *essentials* for fellowship with God and for hearing the "still, small voice." The cutting down on normal brain traffic as a result of going to a mountain or other lonely place to pray, or shutting oneself up in one's private room to commune with the Father in heaven, allows the weak signal from "eternity" to be perceived consciously. The distracting swamping signals from everyday activities must be reduced to allow the "still, small voice" to be heard.

Pathological and Nonpathological Hallucinations

Why are messages pathological? A matter requiring clarification at this point concerns the question of why hallucinations, if they are messages from Mind-at-Large, are often so pathological, or even absurd? Is Mind-at-Large pathological? For hallucinations occur in various types of illness and are mimicked by drug and sensory deprivation. It should be clear, however, that some "hallucinations" may be far from pathological. Peter's "hallucination" reported in Acts 11 was at first mistaken as wrong and pathological by the apostle, who did not initially regard it as a divine vision or message. In fact, he refused to accede to its demands. Later he recognized it for what it was—an important indication of God's will, communicated to him to give him freedom of conscience to eat with and preach to the Gentiles, which as a faithful Jew he was forbidden to do under the old code to which he had hitherto subscribed.

Striking nonpathological hallucinations. The nonpathological nature of some students' LSD hallucinations is sometimes striking. They have "seen eternity" and very sober "reality" under its influence. Others are sure they have "seen" God and the angels. Others again have seen apparent transcendental meaning in the "hedge at the bottom of the garden." That is, ordinary things take on extraordinary, even ineffable, significance. The young men I know who have had these types of experience are usually good students, with no overt pathological traits in their characters—and often little or no religious tendencies in their normal everyday lives. Their experiences often fail to pass into oblivion as do many ordinary dreams. The memory of the experience has often remained and permanently altered the student's outlook on life, often apparently for the better. Such experiences can scarcely be cataloged as pathological.

Approach prophet's visions. Some experiences approach, in a few cases, the type of dream and vision described by the Old and New Testament prophets, which certainly do not appear to be pathological. By their very prophetic fulfilment the biblical visions proved themselves, at least in the eyes of scholarly, conservative commentators, to have been the consequence of actual contact between the prophet's mind and the reality of God's kingdom. That is, the vision proved the reality of true contact with Mind-at-Large by being fulfilled later. The prophet's reduction valve leading to Mind-at-Large seems to have been temporarily less restricted, with the result that the prophet was often overwhelmed with transcendental glory which he later remembered and wrote down. We read that this swamping process often resulted in his falling on his face as one dead.[35]

How can difference be explained? On the other hand, some psychotic LSD experiences are frankly horrible in their pathology. Hopefully, they have little to do with Mind-at-Large or Reality. How, then, can these two types of "hallucinations" (the apparently healthy and the psychotic) be explained if they both arise because the brain is in contact with Mind-at-Large?

The interpretation offered for consideration here is that the message from Mind-at-Large becomes influenced by the reduction valve and nervous system through which it must pass on its way to reaching the deciphering and decoding centers. By its passage through this restriction it may get "twisted" and distorted. A healthy person's "valve" will perhaps not twist and distort the message impulse to the decoding centers, whereas a psychotic's "valve" and brain circuitry may. After all, distortion in the course of transmission can occur in most types of perception. A paranoid schizophrenic may decode a smile from a real friend as the gloating smirk of a man who is bent on persecuting and destroying him.

It is not the impulse itself which matters to consciousness, but the brain's decoding and deciphering of that impulse which makes the impression on our consciousness—or hallucinations of consciousness. Thus, the impulse may pass through the reduction valve safely (whatever that valve may be) and may be perfectly intact as it reaches the brain circuitry (which we can study physiologically). But by the time the impulse has reached and passed the decoding centers in a brain circuit which is defective, the meaning may have become twisted and interpreted as a psychotic experience.

Demonstration of confusion in decoding centers. This possibility of confusion in the decoding centers may be demonstrated in the following simplified way: In the tongue and skin there are various sensory nerve endings, each of which has its special function. Thus, some are taste buds, which only produce a sense of taste (sweet, sour, bitter, etc.) when stimulated. If one of these taste buds is stimulated electrically, the brain does not experience an electric shock, but a taste. Thus a decoding mix-up is occurring, although the impulse itself is perfectly standard.

Some sensory nerve endings respond to heat. If such a "heat" ending is stimulated by a cold rod, it dispatches an impulse to the brain decoding center which registers the impulse generated by the cold as a sensation of heat instead of the cold it is actually experiencing. Similarly, if one treats a pain receptor with a mild amount of heat, its impulse is reported as pain and not as mild heat.

Certain centers in the brain, when stimulated, produce a feeling of well-being. Passing a weak current through them will be interpreted as well-being, and not as an electric shock. So that misinterpretation of impulses, or misdecoding, is known to occur often.

It may be that the same phenomenon occurs in our interpretation of impulses through the reduction valve connecting us with Mind-at-Large, or from proprioception, thus producing pathological hallucinations. This would bear out the practical results of drug experience described in our earlier chapters—the psychotic will probably have a psychotic LSD, mescaline or marijuana experience, whereas the "normal," artistic or sensitive person may have a transcendental experience under otherwise equal conditions. The busy, hardheaded, nonsensitive person may have no drug experience at all—his ordinary proprioceptive impulses are so strong that they will always swamp any and all messages via the reduction valve. So he will declare dogmatically (and correctly for himself) that all these drug and hallucinatory experiences are "bunk." For him they are—and will remain so as long as he remains as he is—swamped with his own proprioceptive egoism.

Pathological and nonpathological hallucinations are both thought to be closely allied to normal dreams in their neural nature. It may therefore clarify the nature of hallucination if we turn our attention to an evaluation of recent research in the area of sleep and dreams.

Paradoxical Sleep, Rapid Eye Movements (REM), Memory and Thought

Dreams as old as history. Dreams, as a form of thought, have mystified, terrified, served as a source of information on the future, and solaced mankind from the dawn of history. Both the Old and New Testament Scriptures emphasize the importance of the dream and the vision. The Old Testament maintains that where there is no vision (or dream) the people cast off restraint (or perish). [36] An outstanding promise of God for the future is that the young men will see visions and the old men will dream, as though dreams and visions were a special gift of God to men on earth. [37]

Psychological importance. Today the generally accepted view of the meaning of dreams and dream thought is that "the dream as portent and prophecy is long out of fashion except among the credulous." [38] Yet in recent years the importance of the dream as a psychological phenomenon in man has been increasingly realized. It is, of course, not considered important that Kekulé conceived the structure of benzene during a daydream on top of a London bus or that Coleridge composed the first lines of "Kubla Khan" in a opium-stimulated dream. [39] It is considered today to be of little import that the Apostle Peter received instructions in a "daydream" to stop despising the heathen as unclean, when God had made them clean. The important consideration today lies in the fact that there does not seem to be much sense to be made out of the contents of the average dream in our day and age apart from the view of Sigmund Freud that "dreams usually reflect wishes stemming from the unconscious; these wishes are repressed demands for instinctual gratification." [40]

Research on dream thought. Today, dream content is considered less important than the dreaming process itself. Let us review briefly some of the modern research which has been carried out on dream thought. All individuals, from the newborn babe onward, seem to dream regularly every night. But only a few are able to *recall* their dreams. It has been found that, on going to sleep, the average sleeper sinks for some sixty to ninety minutes into a deep, dreamless "coma." After this initial period the sleep becomes shallower until it becomes so light that dreaming begins. This fact is disclosed by brain-wave patterns and by rapid eye movements (REM) in the sleeper.

Paradoxical sleep. If the sleeper is awakened when the active brain-wave pattern starts or when the rapid eye movement begins, the dreamer will relate his dream. This state of high activity during sleep is known as paradoxical sleep. By morning the dreamer has usually forgotten the dream completely. During the dream his eyes moved rapidly because he was "watching" his dream pass before him as if it were on a screen. If the dreamer is watching a man climb a ladder, his eyes move up and down. During other "horizontal" action the eyes move from side to side.

Blind people's dreams. Congenitally blind people do not have visual dreams of this kind but dream in the medium of their normal mode of thought, which may be tactile or auditory. The congenitally dumb person may "talk" in his dreams by using sign language with his fingers. If a dream is passive and little action or movement is occurring, there may be no rapid eye movements so that the paradoxical sleep in such cases may be diagnosed only by the brain-wave patterns.

During this dreaming period the brain is as active as it is during waking hours. This state is known as the "emergent" phase and usually lasts for about ten minutes when it arises for the first time in a night. Thereafter, brain activity sinks again to a lower level and becomes dreamless, but the activity is not so low as it was during the first sleep. It stays in this condition for a further sixty to ninety minutes, then rises to a higher level of activity again, during which dreaming again begins, usually accompanied by REM and brain-wave activity. There are usually four or five main dreaming periods during a night, and these periods take up about one-fifth of the total sleeping time. As the night wears on, the dreaming periods become longer, and toward morning they may last up to half an hour.

Dream-poor and dream-rich nights. Some nights hold more dreams than others. However, a dream-poor night is always made up for by a subsequent dream-rich night. The use of alcohol and barbiturates reduces dreaming. After a night under barbiturates or alcohol, dream-rich sleep always follows the next night. Opium and other narcotics are reported to increase the vividness of dreams.[41] About 20 percent of adult sleeping time is invested in dreams. During the first two weeks of life it is believed that babies dream up to 60 percent of any four-hour period. This proportion is reduced to 35 percent during the second half of the first year of life. Two-year-old children dream about 30 percent of their sleeping time, whereas five-year-olds dream about 19 percent of their time asleep. Adolescents at about twenty years of age dream more than any others except neonates and invest 25 percent of their sleeping time in dreams.

Purpose and meaning of dreams. What is the purpose and meaning of dreaming? No unequivocal answer can, at present, be given, although it is known that dreams are essential to health. It may be, however, that the activity of dreaming prevents the brain from sinking into an inactivity so deep that, but for the dream stimulus, there would be no return from it.

As pet owners know, cats and dogs appear to dream in their sleep. Dogs will bark, twitch and show all the signs of the chase while asleep. Cats show similar signs. If, then, dream thought is so universal among the higher animals and man, what purpose might it serve?

Third organismic state. Snyder has characterized paradoxical sleep and REM as the third organismic state of an organism.[42] It is a state distinct from the normal waking and the normal nondreaming sleep state. And while the organism is in this state it responds differently to stimuli than when in the waking or sleeping but nondreaming state. Rats, mice, sheep, goats, cats, dogs, rabbits, monkeys, chimpanzees and opossums all experience this third organismic state. Something similar has been observed in birds, but not as yet in reptiles.

It is thought that the human fetus at a gestational age of twenty-four to thirty weeks spends all its time in this dreaming-sleeping state. The one-day-old neonate spends about 50 percent of its day in this third organismic state.

The gonadal hormones, and therefore their changes in concentration during the cyclic variations of the menstrual cycle, influence paradoxical sleep or the third organismic state. REM time was found to be longest in the late progestational phase. It follows, therefore, that the phase in the menstrual cycle will be likely to influence REM and dreaming in women before the menopause.[43]

Influence of drugs. While discussing the influence of drugs on the third organismic state it should be mentioned that barbiturates reduce REM and, if taken over too long periods of time by psychiatric patients, their dreaming time may be so reduced that a tendency to psychoses and suicide may be demonstrated.[44] This is a known fact of observation, although the explanation on the basis of reduced sleeping time is, of course, not proved. A similar state has been observed in amphetamine abusers. Psychoses are often precipitated if these substances are abused for long periods. This has also been attributed to the chronically reduced dreaming time under amphetamine influence.

The corollary to the observation that opium produces a higher than normal dreaming time during addiction, has not been noted, for no reduction in psychoses due to lengthened dreaming time under opium (opium stimulates particularly vivid and profuse dreaming) has been observed.[45]

Pituitary extract has been noted as causing more frequent dream recall and as producing pleasant, colorful, vivid and generally sanguine dreams. Adrenal extract, on the other hand, produced vivid, unpleasant dreams full of anger and fear. Nitrous oxide (laughing gas) dreams may be characterized by insight and wisdom with flashes of genius. The latter, unfortunately, disappears when exposed to the waking mind. Imipramine and meprobamate act as do the barbiturates in that they both reduce the number of dreams reported per night.[46]

Dream deprivation. William C. Dement and Charles Fisher have carried out extensive studies on dream deprivation in man and have shown that grave consequences can follow the stealing of a subject's dreams.[47] In this work, a patient was awakened every time his EEG (electroencephalogram) pattern or REM showed that he was dreaming. Dreamless sleep was not disturbed. As a control experiment a subject was wakened when he was not dreaming just as often as the dreaming subject was awakened. Thus one subject was deprived of dreaming sleep and the other of a similar amount of dreamless sleep. The experiment was repeated on several pairs of patients. Most persons having their dreams stolen for four consecutive nights refused to continue the experiment. They showed anxiety, irritability and found it difficult to concentrate. Some showed increased appetite and weight gain.

One effort to show how long a healthy young man could go safely without dreaming was very painful to all concerned. After six nights of dream deprivation, the volunteer could no longer be awakened by loud noise or gentle shaking. He did not fall into the usual dreamless sleep which precedes dreaming (normally). His attempts to dream were so continuous that he began to dream within thirty seconds of closing his eyes and had to be disturbed over 200 times (instead of the normal 6-7 times per night to disturb dreaming) in the night. After eight consecutive nights it was impossible to wake the sleeper and he began dreaming almost the instant he closed his eyes. It was impossible to deprive him of his dreams without depriving him entirely of sleep. The implication is that we do not dream simply because we choose to, but because we have to and that we can no more avoid dreaming than we can avoid digestion.[48]

Arise in brain stem. Incredible as it may seem, animals from which the cerebral cortex (the seat of thought and memory) has been removed, apparently still dream. Thus, dreams are thought to arise in the brain stem, the "older" or more primitive part of the brain.

The external events of the day's activities can trigger a dream, and events taking place in a dream are sometimes based on a faulty interpretation of events occurring in the neighborhood of the sleeper. If water is sprinkled onto the sleeper's face he may experience a dream involving falling water. If a bell is rung, he may dream of telephones. Thus, outside events are incorporated, often in a bizarre manner, into a dream. The cortex, which is the censor of our thoughts, is obviously not functioning normally when our dream thought is decoded in this distorted way.

Use of dreams for psychoanalysis. Psychoanalysis based on dreams must, of necessity, be liable to serious defects, if used to interpret the meaning of dreaming for the simple reason that a very low percentage of dreams is recalled at all by the dreamer. Thus the sample of dreams offered to supply the basis for the interpretation of dreams and dreaming is not a representative sample for the psychoanalyst to work on.

In some borderline schizophrenic patients, dream periods made up about 26.5 percent of an average night's sleep compared with 20 percent for a normal person under similar conditions. Dream deprivation in the psychotic tends to intensify the psychosis, which means that a drug producing increased dreaming may reduce the severity of some types of psychosis. Fisher remarks in this connection: "The dream is the normal psychosis and dreaming permits each and every one of us to be quietly and safely insane every night of our lives."[49] In any case, "insane" though dreams may be, they seem to help keep us sane.

Dream Thought and Memory

In the old days Socrates and his disciples conceived of memory and thought as belonging to mind in the same way as a signet ring imprint belongs to a soft wax ball. Memory was thought of as lasting as long as the imprint lasted.

More recently memory has been conceived of as reverberating nerve circuits. An impulse reverberates around one route in the maze of millions of possible nerve-circuit routes, which it then habitually follows. The once-established circuit is then experienced as memory. An original experience burned its way through the as yet unblazed circuit trail to form the original circuit route. The memory of the experience was then supposed to be established as long as this newly blazed trail through brain circuitry was maintained.

Special protein synthesis. These purely electrical ideas have even more recently been replaced by notions of special proteins synthesized in response to special nerve impulses. If DNA structure is slightly modified by an impulse, then a special molecule could be synthesized as a result, which would then function as memory by its presence. That is, according to this concept, memory would be a macromolecular function.

Some evidence has been put forward to support this hypothesis. The experiments using planarian flatworms in support of the above have been more widely publicized than their intrinsic worth perhaps justifies. The flatworms are lowly organisms but possess sufficient neural capacity to enable them by training to learn the route to take to navigate through a maze. After training worms to negotiate the standard maze, two sets of animals were used in an experiment: those trained to negotiate and those not so trained.

When the untrained flatworms were fed upon trained flatworms, it was reportedly found that, with the absorption of the trained flatworm, the untrained worms acquired some knowledge of how to negotiate the standard maze. That is, the experience that the learned dead worm had gained could be passed on to the unlearned worm without being actually learned but merely by the processes of eating and absorption. This would mean that knowledge or thought reside in molecular structure which is passed on by absorption.

These ideas, if true, would be a resurrection of the ancient pagan idea that by cannibalizing one's victim's heart, liver or other physical organs, the eater and victor could acquire the courage and other attributes of the vanquished. It is sufficient to note here that the evidence for the transfer of learning from one flatworm to another by purely physical and chemical means is doubted in many circles today.

Function of brain mucoids in memory. Recent research on the physical and biochemical basis of memory is well summed up in Samuel Bogoch's book which is an attempt to inquire into the function of the brain mucoids in memory.[50] Although this type of research is in its infancy, a few quotes will indicate the direction this kind of inquiry is taking today:

> It should be noted that almost all statements on the coding function of *the nucleic acid in memory assume that a macromolecular product, usually stated to be a protein, results.* The protein is the specific macromolecule which is involved in specific transactions either within the neuron or between neurons. Thus, in the *nucleic acid theories of memory, another macromolecule, usually a protein, constitutes the storage molecule of memory, the actual engram.*
>
> The particular contribution to the theoretical basis of the molecular coding of memory made by this book is the suggestion that the mucoids of the nervous system are involved in the actual encoding of experimental information.
>
> The mucoids would thus act as switching mechanisms, "sign posts" which route transmission. The mucoids would thus be the chemical basis of the make-break mechanisms of the brain's circuitry, the chemical basis of the establishment of the cluster of specific circuits which constitute a memory trace. They might also underlie specificities of contact between glia and neurones.[51]

It is obvious that the whole concept of the physical or molecular basis of memory and thought is still in the melting pot. But physical basis there must be, even though thought itself may be capable of existing supramaterially. Thought still has to be mediated to a physical organism, and a physiological, molecular mechanism for this mediation and transmission would seem to be highly probable and necessary.

Ephemeral Nature of Some Kinds of Thought

One of the difficulties encountered in accounting for dream thought is that it is so ephemeral. The memory of most dreams is so transient that a high percentage is erased forever by the time morning light comes. Unless the sleeper is awakened within ten minutes of the dream as shown by REM, by morning he will possess little remembrance of what has passed through his dreaming mind.

An effort has been made to get around these difficulties by suggesting that there are two kinds of memory, one very short and ephemeral (dream type) and the other much more permanent. But, to date, little has emerged to clarify this important issue. It appears that both electrical and chemical theories will play their part in the final explanation. But, as already pointed out, one point at least has emerged from the present spate of research on dreams—the mind cannot get on without them. They are essential to our nervous system. The sage's report turns out to be more correct than we might have guessed: "Where there is no vision [dream], the people perish [or cast off restraint]."[52]

Stanley Krippner has a chapter in Charles E. Tart's book[30a] entitled "The Psychedelic State, The Hypnotic Trance and the Creative Act" in which he describes the nature of music from other spheres experienced sometimes during psychedelic trips.

[1] C.D. Broad, *Lectures on Psychical Research,* p. 389.
[2] *Ibid.,* p. 339.
[3] I Sam. 28:7.
[4] I Peter 4:6.
[5] II Cor. 12:1-4.
[6] *Ibid.*
[7] Acts 2:3-4, 11; 10:46; I Cor. 12; 14.
[8] Broad, p. 397.
[9] *Ibid.*
[10] *Ibid.,* p. 408.
[11] I Cor. 15; John 20.
[12] John 21:10, 13.
[13] Broad, p. 410.
[14] *Ibid.,* p. 413.
[15] *Ibid.,* p. 416.
[16] *Ibid.,* p. 417.
[17] *Ibid.,* p. 419.
[18] *Ibid.,* p. 423.
[19] A.E. Wilder Smith, *Man's Origin, Man's Destiny,* pp. 25-28 ff.
[20] James T. Culbertson, *The Minds of Robots,* pp. 54-55.
[21] *Ibid.,* p. 60.
[22] *Ibid.,* p. 62.

[23]*Ibid.,* p. 71.

[24]Mark 4:19; Luke 8:14; 21:34.

[25]Eccles. 12:7.

[26]I Sam. 28:17 (RSV).

[27]Deut. 18:9-12 (RSV).

[28]Lev. 19:31 (RSV).

[29]Lev. 20:27 (RSV).

[30]Jer. 27:9 (RSV).

[30a] See Stanley Krippner, "The Psychedelic State, the Hypnotic Trance and the Creative Act," in Charles E. Tart (ed.), *Altered States of Consciousness,* pp. 272-273.

[31]Brewster Ghiselin (ed.), *The Creative Process.*

[32]Acts 10.

[33]Dan. 9:3.

[34]II Cor. 12:1-5.

[35]Dan. 8:17; 10:6-9; I Cor. 14:25.

[36]Prov. 29:18.

[37]Acts 2:17.

[38]*The Anatomy of Sleep,* p. 60.

[39]Milton Kramer, *et al.,* "The Influence of Drugs on Dreams" in Andrew Herxheimer (ed.), *Drugs and Sensory Functions,* p. 312.

[40]Benjamin B. Wolman, *The Unconscious Mind,* p. 15.

[41]Kramer, *et al., ibid.*

[42]*Ibid.,* p. 300.

[43]T. Benedek and B.B. Rubenstein, *Psychosexual Functions in Women.*

[44]Kramer, *et al.,* p. 309.

[45]*Ibid.*

[46]*Ibid.,* p. 314.

[47]William C. Dement and Charles Fisher, *Further Experimental Studies on Dreaming.*

[48]*The Anatomy of Sleep,* pp. 77-78.

[49]*Ibid.,* p. 81.

[50]Samuel Bogoch, *The Biochemistry of Memory.*

[51]*Ibid.,* pp. 89, 90, 216.

[52]Prov. 29:18.

11. The Importance of Motivation

LSD Is Not Antisocial

Frank Barron maintains that many of the younger generation take LSD simply as a form of social protest.[1] They are
dissatisfied with the condition of their society, and LSD trips
are their way of protesting against it. While this may be true
in some cases it should not be construed to mean that LSD is,
of necessity, an antisocial drug.

LSD, when correctly used, is not antisocial and may be
used to good advantage therapeutically. Indeed, under some
circumstances it may be used to restore to society individuals
who had been antisocial, such as alcoholics. It is purely the
abuse of the drug which makes for the antisocial effects.
Thus, antisocial individuals may, with others, take advantage
of LSD trips to escape from a society they detest. The
Establishment may regard such escapism as antisocial, but
who can judge or condemn those who wish to escape from a

society they abhor? Who is going to decide that it is a bad thing to want escape from certain ways of life and forms of society? For there are many thinking people who, after sober reflection, would also like to get away from the present Western rat race. To conclude that LSD is an antisocial drug merely because people use it as a means of escape is to misconstrue the problem.

Why Drugs?

The problem is profound and cannot be simply dismissed under the label "antisociety" or "protest by the younger generation." As we see it, the problem resolves itself into the following question, if protest or escapism are at all relevant in LSD abuse: What induces such a high percentage of the more intelligent members of our younger generation to start taking drugs, when there are plenty of other, perhaps more effective, means of protesting against or escaping from society? The mere fact that many do use other means of protest and escapism such as rioting, joining the hippies or yippies or beatnik movements, police baiting, and writing underground protest literature, shows that other means of protest are on hand and available for use. However, a good proportion of intelligent students and other rebels deliberately choose the drug method, which acts on themselves and not on the society against which they protest.

This is therefore the question: Why drugs? More specifically, what is there in modern Western society which makes personal drug abuse so attractive compared with other means of escape or protest? It must be remembered that it is the modern, affluent, Western society which seems especially prone to spawn drug epidemics. Recent tendencies in England, Switzerland, Germany, Sweden and the United States (to mention a few such societies) have demonstrated this fact rather conclusively. Eastern countries such as India have experienced drug problems for centuries—but not adolescent drug epidemics on the scale which confronts present Western society. The question becomes more urgent when it is remembered that some of the drugs used are thought to be less than innocuous both to the present and to future generations.

Nonmaterial Values and Necessities

To maintain purely physical health, one needs adequate nourishment, exercise and a sound genetic constitution. Today, however, a good deal of strong evidence shows that man needs more than purely physical and chemical constituents for total health. Health needs more than the correct proteins, amino acids and vitamins in the diet. More is needed to produce a healthy human specimen than a perfect set of genes, though this is certainly essential. Suitable environment with which the genes can "react" is needed in addition to all this. Certain nonphysical and nonchemical factors have to be present to satisfy man's total health needs. Supplying a man with every known physical requirement will not satisfy him or maintain his total health if he is, for example, deprived of his liberty.

Liberty an Essential Ideal

Our forefathers knew the value of liberty. Rather than be deprived of this one ingredient in their psychical diet—liberty—they left forever their old homelands, friends and customs to make a new start in a strange and distant land. Life was intolerable to them without liberty and they would rather have died than forfeit it. Many feel the same way today. For them it is intolerable to reflect that millions of men and women in today's so-called enlightened world are vegetating their lives away under political systems which, as a matter of principle, deprive man of this liberty—one of his most basic rights and necessities.

Liberty is not as easy to define and to measure as calories or minimal daily vitamin requirements. Yet, although liberty is a somewhat intangible concept from a merely materialistic point of view, it is certainly a vitally important component to most people for their physical as well as mental development.

Above his tangible material needs (very real, of course) man has intangible ones, which are just as real, such as liberty, creativity, love, happiness and a sense of beauty. If these needs are not met, both physical and psychical illnesses may be precipitated. No useful purpose is served in denying these intangible needs simply because they do not fit into pure materialistic philosophy. Let us be sure of this, that both the material and the intangible needs of man are real needs.

This ingredient in man's "diet" which we have called liberty, is apparently so important that the Bible maintains it to be a property and attribute of God himself. For that source of information tells us that "where the Spirit of the Lord is, there is liberty [freedom]."[2] We are also reminded that "if the Son ... shall make you free, ye shall be free indeed."[3] In some church services God the Father is classified as the "Author of perfect freedom." Now if God is the Author of freedom, then it becomes obvious why liberty is likely to be a necessity in the "diet" of man, whom he has made. For liberty, being a divine attribute, is therefore part of the divine concept of man's nature, for man is made in God's image.

In addition to this intangible known as liberty there are other related intangibles which must be added to the list of necessities for humans. To be in a position to discuss these we must first look at some purely physical functions of the body.

THE SIGNIFICANCE OF TONUS

Muscle Challenge

We are so constructed physically that our muscles need constant challenge for the maintenance of muscular health. When flexor muscles pull against extensor muscles, a muscular tonus, or tension, is produced. Because of this tonus or "tone" we can accurately use our wrists and fingers to write, thread needles and do other delicate or intricate work. One muscle, exactly balancing out its fellow, produces a marvelously sensitive mechanism for mechanical accuracy. But over and above mere accuracy there is another important consideration. If a muscle is not constantly challenged by the pull of its opposite number, muscle health and tone are lost. Degeneration or atrophy sets in. Constant challenge, the constant pull of the muscle against the other, is the essential to muscular health.

Biochemical and Chemical Balance

This question of tone, tension or balance is not confined only to muscular and mechanical matters in the body. It applies also to the biochemical and chemical balance of the body as well. The female sex hormones, for example, are exactly balanced against the male sex hormones in both the male and the female bloodstream. Disturbance of this biochemical tonus or balance may precipitate serious physical or even mental ailments. In fact, cancer is thought to be precipitated in some cases if this sex hormonal challenge is upset. Similarly, the sugar and water metabolism of the body is regulated by a balanced challenge between the various hormones concerned in this area. In all these cases one hormone exactly balances out the other and, by means of suitable feedback mechanisms, the correct equilibrium is maintained.

Nervous System

Even the nervous system shows the same principle of challenge and tonus. The vegetative nervous system demonstrates the relationship between the sympathetic nervous system and its partner, the parasympathetic nervous system. For the sympathetic nervous system, when stimulated, produces raised blood pressure, more rapid heartbeat and a contraction of the arterioles. On the other hand, stimulation of the parasympathetic nervous system produces effects which neutralize sympathetic stimulation. Lowered blood pressure, slowing of the heartbeat rate and dilation of the arterioles results. Thus the sympathetic nervous system counterbalances and challenges the parasympathetic nervous system, one system holding the other in check. Disturbance of this equilibrium or tonus in the nervous system can precipitate serious ailments involving blood pressure and cardiac disorders.

Thus, in order to maintain his well-being, a man needs not only a nutritionally balanced diet. He must also have a correctly balanced internal tone, both as far as the biochemistry of his hormonal concentration is concerned as well as between the parts of his vegetative nervous system. For these tensions and challenges, both hormonal and biochemical as well as neural, are just as necessary as the adequate supply of vitamins, amino acids and minerals.

Mental Challenge

It is, however, not only in the physiology, biochemistry and vegetative nervous systems of the body that constant challenge and tension are basic health requirements. A man's mind needs just as much challenge and tonus as his body systems. Put a man on a "soul destroying" job such as tightening down "bolt No. 492" as he stands for years at a conveyor belt in an automobile assembly plant. The lack of challenge in such a purely mechanical job will surely make itself felt in the course of time. The man will not only become frustrated, but he is likely to wither mentally. His character is in danger of attrition unless he obtains some other activities or hobbies which offer him the sense of challenge and tonus he lacks in his boring daily work. A man's mind needs resistance to work against, just as a muscle needs the resistance of its fellow muscle in order to maintain and to develop itself. A mental challenge is just as important for the mind as a muscular challenge is for a man's body. Unless he experiences these constant and regular stresses and challenges he is in danger of deterioration, just as a muscle without the challenge of tonus deteriorates. All kinds of mysterious ailments set in for the man who is forced to live like a vegetable, without challenge. Man is not a vegetable and was never intended to be one. Challenge, stress and tension, then, are essential factors in our mental fare, just as freedom is an essential.

Here again, the Bible fully supports these considerations. For it says that it is *good* for a man to bear the *yoke* in his youth.[4] In our education and training it is good for us to feel the pull of responsibility and high goals with their inbuilt tension and resistance. We are so constructed that physically and mentally we need resistance to overcome, challenge to meet. When we have done our part in resisting the tensions, be they physical or psychical, we are rewarded with a sense of achievement and well-being. Frustration from which so many suffer today comes from overcoming, working against and achieving *less* than we set out to do, achieving *less* than we could achieve. The glow of satisfaction which comes after we have reached a goal is an intangible, vital necessity to bodily and psychical health.

Thus science has shown us in the past hundred years that a large part of nature, ourselves included, is set up to function on the basis of the supplying of material needs and the meeting of intangible requirements such as liberty, self-expression, the ability to meet challenge, to bear a yoke with success, to achieve an aim or to resist a tension. Both the tangibles as well as the intangibles are essentials to physical and mental health. Inability to meet the need for tangibles or intangibles brings with it ailments which are typical for each kind of unfulfilled need.

To complete the picture of human needs which must be met if total health (physical as well as psychical) is to be attained, two other important requirements must be mentioned here.

Dreaming—The Need for Freedom of Thought and Vision

We have already pointed out the vital role which dreaming plays in the matter of mental health. Our necessity for untrammeled dreaming reflects the mind's requirement for the unhindered exercise of imagination and thought. Dream thought is thought which is not restricted by such trifles as material reality. Dreaming is free from the necessity of responding to actual afferent nerve impulses. That is, it appears to be largely independent of the body's proprioception and has little to do with the material reality surrounding us and communicated by our nervous system. From what we have already said on the subject of liberty and self-expression it is therefore perhaps not surprising that free dreaming is a vital requirement for health. This amounts to the astonishing fact that we actually need the facility of becoming "insane" or "visionary" every night of our lives as we dream unhindered. Thus this right to dream and "have visions" must be added to our list of intangibles for total health.

All these intangible matters are no less real than the tangible, material ones insofar as they concern our well-being. In the last analysis we might perhaps class the nonmaterial matters as ideals. Liberty may certainly be classed as an ideal; so is the meeting of challenge an idealistic virtue; so is self-expression in the form of love or artistic creativity. The right to become a "visionary" every night as we dream is certainly a necessity, and the true dreamer or visionary is usually an idealist. The point we wish to make here is that it is a basic human right to have ideals, to love freedom and to strive for the liberty of untrammeled human thought. Without these basic rights we shrivel.

Survival in Eternity, an Ennobling Ideal

To the above-mentioned imponderables and intangibles may be added one more. Every man knows that in the natural course of events he will die after he has lived out his years. He has no personal experience of what happens at death and after death and can probably give no sound personal reasons for believing either in survival after death or in total dissolution. Yet the average man clings to the concept of survival after death and longs for immortality. It seems, as we have already pointed out, as if God planted in every man's heart the idea of eternity and personal survival in it.[5] A large proportion of ordinary people are bound by their fear of death all their lives.[6] They long for life which will last forever away from the trials of the everyday jungle of earthly life in which "achievement" is so ephemeral. The ideal of everlasting life in the presence of their Maker is nourished in the minds of men and women of many religions and cultures although the postulated mechanism for the attainment of that life varies from religion to religion. But the conviction that there will be a period of largeness of life and liberty after the strait jacket of earthly life has been thrown off, has been a vital ideal in man's history through many ages. Such an ideal has raised and ennobled man from the dawn of time.

This is seen in the elaborate burial rites practiced by early man, to show that he cared for the departed one for whom he made the preparations for the afterlife. Belief in survival and in eternity obviously helped to trigger a lack of selfishness which led the surviving members of the family or tribe to sacrifice food, jewels or utensils for the departed one's journey. Thus the concept of eternity and of man's survival in it seems to have improved or elevated man's character. If this is the case, even the idealistic concept of eternity may be necessary for psychic health. Certainly where neither belief in God nor eternity is present, and where atheism and materialism reign supreme, brutality often takes over—as in Communist China today.

THE SECULARIZATION OF SOCIETY

Meeting Physical Needs

All these nonmaterial values and necessities are mentioned here to demonstrate their essential contribution to health in addition to the better known material aids. If anything is certain, it is surely that Western affluent society is outdoing itself in its efforts to satisfy—or shall we say satiate?—its own material needs. From every side, from the morning breakfast table to supper at night, we hear of our need for vitamins and minerals, for clothes, houses, furniture, cars, air conditioning and other material comforts. But let us remember that the satisfaction of these material needs represents only the material side of man. The intangible needs of his spiritual component must be met just as conscientiously as his material needs to aim at total "hybrid" health, for as we have noted, man is a hybrid of matter and spirit.

Spiritual Needs Unmet

Would it be true to maintain that man's nonmaterial spiritual needs are being met in our affluent Western society as well and as completely as his physical needs? The difficulty is that the material needs can be bought in the supermarkets and the drug and department stores, and that wealthy companies can become wealthier by supplying these needs. Material needs lend themselves to commercialization, whereas the supply of the intangible spiritual needs of challenges and ideals are not, apparently, as lucrative or attractive to the competitive businessman. Have the needs for real liberty of spirit, for challenge and achievement, for unhindered creative thought and idealistic vision been met and investigated in the same way that nutritional needs have been? What research is going in the area of challenge, and the development of character? Has the youngster in today's affluent society had the opportunity and teaching to enable him to reflect profitably on the effect of challenge on character development? Or even on eternity in his own heart? Or has the same youngster been driven to distraction by the necessity to conform in thought and in education and by the prospect of the rat race afterward?

It is my personal conviction that Western society in becoming progressively organized is becoming at the same time progressively denuded of personal liberty, imagination and challenge. Increasing secularization of society is bringing with it increasing restrictions on personal liberty, challenge and imagination. Materialism of the rankest sort is taking over and depersonalizing us. Idealism is discounted, indeed, it may often be looked upon* as dangerous in individuals. Anything tending toward a transcendental view of life or experience is rapidly becoming suspect in today's atmosphere.

The Mystic Ousted

Clergyman and intellectual. In the older societies the mystic, who spent a lifetime contemplating God and his works and who thereby gathered a wisdom unknown to his more prosaic fellows, was an integral part of society. Society accepted him as an idealist, fed him, revered him and learned from him. But in Western society today one of the lowest paid (and, therefore, least respected) members of society is the counterpart of the old mystic, the clergyman. After him in order of unproductiveness in the eyes of some segments of society comes the intellectual. Unfortunately today's clergyman is too often an unworthy counterpart of his forerunner the mystic, for the parson has a family to feed, and bills to pay, which means more often than not, he has to moonlight instead of spending his spare time in prayer to God, in study and in contemplation of him and his works. Today's intellectual, too, is often a mere shadow of his former self, as we saw him in other societies. For he too is often a negative shadow, a revolutionary of the "pink" persuasion who recklessly criticizes the society that (scarcely) supports him.

Thus, there is little left in the way of guidance for the younger generation as far as a supply of the intangible necessities of the human spirit is concerned. In wide areas of our generation the clamor of commerce is heard arguing for the supplying of the purely physical needs of the body—the hormone, the vitamin and the contraceptive pill.

Distortion of values. The progressive secularization of society today emphasizes this distortion of values. It is surely not by accident that Iron Curtain socialism is atheistic in outlook. Western socialism also, when it is not agnostic, is usually atheistic. Our society is interested in the material as opposed to the transcendental needs of man. Under the cloak of bettering the physical lot of the race, improving every man's earning capacity, enriching the material comfort of his home, reinforcing his nutrition, bettering his facilities for play and recreation, and modernizing his working conditions so that he can produce more for less effort, man's intangible needs are progressively ignored. But this drive to improve man's material lot, often at the expense of his idealistic fate, has brought with it a marked tendency to the depersonalization of man himself.

A Mold for the Masses

Depersonalization. The secular state, if it is going to care for the masses from the cradle to the grave, must fit every individual into the same mass mold. In other words, it must depersonalize him. If cradles and graves are to be supplied for all, then cradles and graves, like political thought, must be standardized. Woe to the poor individual who does not fit this mold or method of thought! If the secular state is going to supply education for all, then education must be geared to suit the masses and not the gifted and unusual individual. That is, education must be geared to the slowest or, at best, the average student, so that all can creep along together at the slowest pace, and excellence is penalized. Small allowance is made for the fact that all men are different and are, in fact, not born equal. That is, they are not born with equal gifts, though they should have equal rights to progress. If the secular state is going to look after us all, then the state must have wide powers over us all and we must be subjects to its all-planning and all-embracing program. It is no wonder then that excellence as opposed to the average in achievement is becoming rare, no wonder that the individual human is becoming depersonalized and forced into the mold of the mass. He has been robbed of his initiative. And if man is being depersonalized, why not depersonalize God too? Thus God has become no longer the Person he was, but an anonymous spirit in some all-pervading dimension leading to oblivion.

Some excellent ideas. Some of the basic ideas behind the modern secular state are excellent. No man or woman should avoidably go hungry or be without the education necessary to fit him for modern society. The fact that the socialists of the modern secular society promise to meet these perfectly obvious and pressing needs disarms us. The motive is so obviously good. The real difficulties in the scheme become visible only in the course of time and arise from the bitter fact that it is necessary to regiment large masses of the people in order to realize such schemes. Regimentation of individuals is the first price we have to pay for the material advantages accruing from free education, social security, medicare, etc. If one wishes to observe the effects of regimentation on the common people one only need observe life today in Soviet Russia or Communist China or make a study of life under Hitler in the 1930's.

Red Tape—The Problem of Bureaucracy

The second price that has to be paid for "free" material services is that of the colossal waste of time and manpower observable wherever the secularized state sets up its government of the people. We find whole regiments of men and women doing "work" of a kind which no private industry would ever countenance if it did not wish to court bankruptcy. The kind of unproductive "work" involved in running bureaucracy is so well known that we need waste no time here describing it. If the state supplies anything, a truckload of papers and forms will need to be filled out before the head of any department can allow the head of another department to go ahead with the launching of his truckload of papers. The cost of the finished article, after all these administrative costs have been added to the cost of the manufacture of the article, is such that no private industry could ever consider buying it. But the taxpayer is forced to buy the article with taxes which soar chronically wherever the state takes over.

Our immediate concern is with the effect which this vast

waste of time and material has on the quality of the lives of the people who run it. The army of officials concerned in tending this huge idling machine has to handle the tons of paper and forms daily in just about the same way that our assembly line man in the automobile factory tightens down bolt No. 492. Hundreds of clerks can be kept choring away at "paper jobs" all their lives without any concrete achievement to show for it. The huge system that man is building up, and the desire for maximum specialization, and therefore for economy, have combined to take challenge and motivation out of both kinds of jobs.

Regimentation in Institutes of Higher Learning

A similar attitude to life has invaded large sectors of society today. This development is by no means a preserve of government-ridden countries. In the universities of past years the student was personally well known to his tutor or professor. There was enough leisure and opportunity to discuss problems affecting the student's total education and future. As a result of this relationship between the teacher and the student, lifelong friendships often arose to the enrichment of the life and character of both parties. The idealism of the professor (if he was an idealist) spurred on the student, and the student's hard work encouraged the professor. Obviously the discussion of ideas and values colored the whole relationship between the two.

Large classes. Today, in our huge state universities, the professor's classes are so large that he cannot be reasonably expected to know all his students' names, let alone to personally grade their examination papers. One potent cause of rioting and unrest among students in the United States today is the tendency of professors to shove their lecturing responsibilities onto their graduate students. The undergraduate student then feels that he has been short-changed. He came to the university to study under a famous professor—not under some unknown graduate student. One well-known institution of higher learning employs 4,500 professors, associate and assistant professors, instructors and graduate students with their auxiliary staff to look after the academic needs of some 2,500 graduate and undergraduate students. And still some professors' classes number over one hundred at each session! Because of the administrative (read "bureaucratic") pressures on the professor, he is still relieved if he can farm out at least some of his lecturing to his graduate students, for the actual teaching staff is still hopelessly inadequate.

Huge administration. The secret of this administrative miracle is not very well hidden. It lies in the huge administration, involving tons of paper daily, which often has political overtones, runs for administration's sake and has nothing whatsoever to do with academic teaching. The university has become a state within a state and its teaching functions are becoming ever less important, while its "social" functions are ever increasing. Football teams seem to be more important than faculty members, and the coach will often receive a far higher salary than any academic staff member. Radio stations must be run, with their huge budgets, managers and technicians. Public relations offices swell the merry band—all at the taxpayers' expense in the case of the state university.

Hires graders. In such a situation the professor is forced to mark his examination paper by proxy. He employs undergraduates by the hour to lay transparent answer keys over the students' examination papers (which incidentally, possess a remarkable resemblance to income tax or immigration forms). To save time, the student merely has to insert checks at the appropriate spaces in the columns. He seldom has to write an essay, for the professor has not the time to grade essays. They are "subjective" and not "objective" in any case and so may be rejected as a means of assessing a student's ability. Of course, putting check marks on forms completes the student's downward career to illiteracy, for he seldom learns to write an essay or to express himself in any other way except by "filling out the form" pushed in front of him.

Thus the student is conditioned to accept abject bureaucracy.

This is a reason why many schoolteachers find it difficult to express themselves either in writing or in speech. The grading student who lays the transparencies over the examination papers often knows nothing of the subject matter of the examination. His job is merely to check positions on columns blindly and mechanically, and grade the paper accordingly. When X is in the correct blank he gives full marks and when it is not he gives zero. What could be a challenging opportunity to learn something of a new subject, to experience the thoughts and conclusions of other students, may thus be converted into a boring chore hardly fit for a kindergarten or a mental institution.

Students become machines. By making large institutions of higher learning subject to the laws of "efficient" big business and secular administration, a great deal of idealism, imagination and challenge has been blotted out of higher learning. Students, both those being examined and those who grade the examinations, have become machines. Both student and professor have become depersonalized—and often bored to tears. Glorious intellectual challenge and opportunity for learning and vision have been prostituted to a depersonalizing machine. A depersonalized person does not believe in persons, so he will ride roughshod over them. Neither does he believe in a personal God. He believes in nothing except depersonalized machines to control others. No wonder he feels frustrated, and riots.

Produces drug epidemic. Why have we looked at these aspects of modern society in our survey of drugs and the drug epidemic? One common factor has already emerged as important in shaping the kind of modern life that has produced the drug epidemic. The individual is being forced to fit into mass schemes and is in process of being depersonalized. Even such expressions as "drafting young men into the armed forces and *processing* them" shows just how far the state has gone in achieving this depersonalization. It involves the loss of the glorious individual freedom which is the right of all men. Vision, sense of challenge and even religious involvement with a personal God—all are in dire danger of vanishing today.

As a result of the loss of idealism, young society is showing signs of sickness, psychical sickness. Society is satiated by the lush and ever present supply of material tangibles but is starved for spiritual or psychical intangibles of personal liberty, personal worth, right to indulge in "dreaming" of the idealistic kind, the right to personal achievement and fulfillment, the right to be different. Even man's religion, which has to do with his native idealism, is in danger of being starved of intangible spiritual or psychical food, while being flooded out by materialistic satiation. This is the environment in which the drug epidemic has been spawned, along with the waves of riots, arson, police baiting and other signs of a sick society. *No police repression, no drives to law and order are going to suppress this, because one cannot suppress the symptoms of sickness by force.* They have to be cured by changing the conditions which led to the sickness.

THE CAUSES AND SYMPTOMS OF THE DRUG EPIDEMIC

Man Becomes a Mechanism

From what we have already discussed it begins to look as if man, under the pressure of the state and the affluent society, is in danger of becoming a mere depersonalized reflex hydraulic mechanism in the service of his own material needs and those of humanity. Man feeds into his perceptive nervous system certain impulses and out come the muscular twitchings leading to "productivity" for which he receives his pay and food. He runs, answers the telephone, says "yes" or "no" in the interests of the superbusiness which employs him. Or he gains grades in the examination his society sets him by putting the correct check marks in the right columns and spaces of his income-tax-form-like examination papers.

No room for personal plans or ideas. A great deal of the personal activity of many in our society has little to do with personal decision or achievement at all. Indeed, personal consultation with his conscience might be highly undesirable in the eyes of the superorganization employing him. The employee must keep steadily before his mind's eye the solid fact that he is employed only as a kind of intelligent reflex servomechanism and operates primarily for the material profit of the society within society which employs him. Personal plans or ideas are not permitted to conflict with the interests of the superorganization for which he dances for pay and possibly recognition.

Perhaps we are guilty of exaggeration, but the fact remains that the situation described above is true at least in principle. In fact, many of us have to face up to just this kind of situation. In the interests of the material welfare of our own society we are being progressively robbed of some of our most basic spiritual and psychical necessities for a fulfilled life. Our material needs are often being paid for by the sacrifice of some basic psychical needs. Thus the inherent need for mental, spiritual or psychical tone and challenge is being endangered by the society we are fast building.

Little employee initiative. The businessman and employer will rightly maintain that the average employee today shows little responsibility or initiative on the job. The fact is, of course, that many employees do fit into this unflattering picture both in their work and leisure time. For the affluent society has reduced many of its members to such a state of apathy by its lack of anything but material challenge that they tend to sink into a kind of thoughtless, goalless stupor. Challengeless work, sitting out office hours and working by the clock, together with the endless tedium of purely mechanical, repetitive activity, produce a kind of general mental anesthesia.

Unsatisfactory leisure time. Over and above these consider-ations comes the fact that the educational systems of today teach their pupils little of how to use leisure time effectively and satisfyingly. The result is that both working and leisure time are frittered away thoughtlessly, or wasted on vicarious stimulation which many films and TV programs provide. The mass psychoses seen in some commercialized ball games are examples. (Not a word shall be said, however, against the genuine satisfaction and achievement attained by the stimulus of actually playing in a ball game. This brings us to the question of physiology and the role played by exercise in today's mechanized society.)

Soul-starvation. It is this soul-starvation, this loss of personal human values, which is a prime factor, we believe, in the precipitation of epidemics of drug abuse among the younger members of our society. They are unable to subsist on a purely material diet and are thus forced to look elsewhere—to drugs in this case—for psychical satisfaction on a supramaterial basis. For hallucinogenic drugs lift them, as it were, to another world where they are seemingly in contact with Mind-at-Large, and experience, firsthand, transcendental realities.

Deterioration a Result of Lack of Tonus

Thrive on challenge. If the tonus of a muscle system, consisting of extensor and flexor pairs, is destroyed and the mutual challenge of one muscle against another is removed, then both kinds of muscles begin to degenerate. For both flexors and extensors thrive on the mutual challenge which each affords the other, as well as on the purely physical nutrition brought to them by their blood supply. Can anything be done to hinder this degeneration of the flexors and extensors once the tonus has been reduced or removed? There are only two possibilities to attain this end: restoration of the muscle tonus or challenge, and/or stimulation of the muscles artificially (e.g., electrically), so that an artificial tonus or challenge is built up.

To flourish, the muscle must be stimulated or challenged by something. It must pull and be pulled if it is to avoid degeneration. Therefore, when the normal physiological challenge of extensor-flexor tonus is removed or reduced, something must be done to replace the natural challenge which is lacking, and artificial stimulation must be resorted to. If such artificial stimulation is regularly practiced the muscle may be retained in a reasonable state of health, even though the natural tonus has been reduced or removed.

Applied to lack of psychical challenge. These observations can be applied by analogy to the question and problem of lack of psychical challenge in modern life. As we have already noticed, a large proportion of real, healthy challenge has been removed from man's life in the affluent supersociety of today. Will this reduction of psychical tone produce symptoms in the mental challenge system similar to what we have seen in muscle challenge systems? It begins to look as if the psyche, or shall we say, the moral fibre system, may be beginning already to undergo a degeneration analogous to that which we have already seen in our muscle systems. A flabbiness of tone and moral fibre seems to be setting in already. How else can one explain the New Morality, which is no morality at all when one comes down to an analysis of it? Psychical tone has been unbalanced by the monstrous, mechanized system Western man himself has built up and, as a result, his moral fibre has become flabby. The discipline necessary to respect law and other people's rights and property has become so weakened that the police can with difficulty restrain the lawlessness which is taking over on all sides. In this same light the ruthless anarchy of riots—even police riots—strikes, robberies and lootings can be understood. They would seem to be the result of the general flabbiness and impotence of moral tonus which is developing all around us. Wrong is no longer wrong, and right is but relative in this weakened system.

Locating the Trouble

Society is impotent in stopping trend. We all know that something is wrong with society—and with ourselves. But most of us experience difficulty in putting our finger on the exact spot at which the trouble is brewing. The more the situation deteriorates, the more impotent we feel to remedy it. All sorts of plans are made, crime commissions appointed and studies made, but crimes such as the cold-blooded murder of a President and of his brother, of a Negro leader and of ordinary citizens, etc., goes on. Society is impotent to stop the trend to degeneracy or the years of carnage in Asia under both the French and the Americans.

Here, again, the situation bears a remarkable analogous similarity to that of a man who has had his muscle tonus destroyed or reduced. Such a man feels his weakness; he knows something is wrong. But the more the deterioration of the muscle systems sets in, the more he feels himself to be unable to cope with the difficulty. He has not the strength. It is being sapped from within—not from any want of material nutrition, but from sheer want of challenge. The result is an ever increasing impotence, an ever increasing inability to halt the creeping paralysis. For he is suffering from progressive paralysis, just as our society is suffering from progressive paralysis of the moral fibre. The "muscular dystrophy" resulting from the first situation resembles the "moral fibre dystrophy" affecting our modern society.

Two ways of halting degeneration. There are only two ways of putting a stop to this degeneration. First, to restore the psychical tone by restoring to the individual his dignity and the right to challenge and achievement. If we succeed in doing this the "moral fibre" will restore itself—that is, if degeneration has not gone too far.

The other alternative is to stimulate the psychical tone artificially, to produce an artificial challenge, just as we obtained the effect of a restored muscle tone by artificial stimulation in muscle pairs suffering from reduced tone. That is, if the genuine psychical tone or challenge has been removed or dangerously reduced, then artificial challenge must be resorted to if the "muscle" system of moral fibre is to avoid total degeneration.

Drugs and Artificial Stimulation

Resort to artificial means. Society, particularly young

society, which is the most sensitive part of it and feels the symptoms of sickness creeping over it early, is resorting to artificial stimulation of various types to avoid the flabbiness and impotence of impending decay. One kind of artificial stimulation is found in the use of hallucinatory and other drugs to obtain the extra "kicks" which cannot be obtained from the natural stress of life in suburbia. Another kind of stimulation consists in precipitating conflict with the police in riots, provocation, arson and looting—or driving through red traffic lights to see what gives way first. Then there is the more harmless "kick" of the various forms of vicarious excitement and achievement experienced in watching football and other ball games. All these methods and activities provide artificial "kicks," artificial stimuli, which the organism demands because of the rarity of genuine challenge.

Dreaming the missing dreams. The hallucinatory drugs literally provide the user with the faculty of dreaming the dreams which are missing from real (drab) life today. The visions with which affluent society cannot provide its younger generation are experienced in a substitute form with the aid of LSD, mescaline or marijuana. If young and old cannot legally and normally obtain some sort of genuine excitement and challenge, then they will seek it by any means available to them, in many cases from drugs.

In short, these drugs—together with many of the other stimuli to which the affluent society is heir today, such as violence, crime, sex abuse and anarchy—do furnish a source of challenge, interest, visions and dreams, together with the challenge of danger, for which the human spirit was built and without which it often does not operate normally. For the uncomfortable fact is that the human spirit was built for real, genuine achievement, which involves concomitant danger and challenge. It was not built for the artificial "kicks" of drugs, nor was it designed for artificial or "synthetic" challenge.

Psyche can distinguish. The human psyche can distinguish with ease between the substitute and the genuine challenge, and only the genuine challenge is truly satisfying to man.

That is, the substitute does not provide a true, effective satisfaction, as the use of the substitute in drug abuse has shown. For abuse of drugs of any sort may lead to illness. Drug abuse in areas of central nervous stimulation or depression can lead to severe mental illness. But true challenge (I do not mean "worry"), unlike the synthetic challenge of centrally active drugs, rarely leads to moral or mental breakdown.

Other Synthetic Stimuli

Another complicating factor arises in conditions of affluence. As already pointed out, the synthetic stimuli which certain drugs afford can have drastic consequences. Other synthetic stimuli available to and used by our affluent society can also have dangerous consequences. The need for excitement and challenge can be satisfied to some extent by vicarious experience via television or radio or films. The violence, crime, tension and sex seen through these means of mass communication show the basic need of the human psyche for "tonus." Unfortunately, the appetite for the "real thing" is whetted by having the substitute continually dangled before one's eyes. The male adolescent who continually sees the image of lightly clad young women on the screen will not rest until he has the "real thing" in his grasp. Since one earns the "real thing" (on the screen, at least) by "bravery" and violence, the young adolescent may unconsciously come to the conclusion that this is the way things are done.

Thus, although artificial stimulation fulfills a need in maintaining tonus, yet it is only a substitute and can therefore only show the various consequences of substitutes in general. For substitutes for the genuine can lead to perverted appetites. In this respect the hallucinatory drugs can often create a twisted desire for that which real life and genuine religious experience should supply in a natural way.

The Problem of Delayed Challenge

The extent to which challenge has reached imbalance in

our modern society seems to be understood only dimly today. One realizes that it is not merely challenge—challenge pure and simple—of which we have been robbed. The challenge situation has become increasingly more subtle, especially in recent years. It is true that the challenge of achievement has been taken from us in many ways with the resultant degeneration of "moral fibre." But after this degeneration has become widespread and the "moral muscle" has begun to become "flabby," then another trick is frequently played on our younger generation. Into this trick of modern society we must now look very briefly.

Youth not prepared. There may be a young man or woman who has never been exposed to much real challenge and whose metaphorical "flexors and extensors" have never had much chance of development by use, who may, in young adulthood, be suddenly and traumatically exposed to a plethora of challenge, strain and tension, demand for decision and withstanding of stress, with which he simply cannot cope. He has been so coddled by the affluent society during most of his adolescent years, has become so physically "soft" in overheated rooms in winter or air-conditioned rooms in summer, with cars to take him everywhere and a generous allowance, that he has not developed the necessary "hardness of muscle" to meet the stress of new, unexpected situations. The new trauma may be marital adjustment with the sweet young thing he has married early (on father's money), who has, like her husband, always been used to having her own way. Or he may be sent to Vietnam to meet a ruthless, pitiless enemy hardened by a lifetime of jungle warfare. Of course, it is no fault of our young man or woman when a breakdown occurs. The process he or she is being subjected to resembles that of stopping the development of leg muscle flexors and extensors in a child by preventing the child from learning to walk.

Too much luxury. Some time ago I was shown around the new dormitories of a small liberal arts college of excellent reputation. My justifiably proud guide showed me sumptuous suites of rooms for both guests and students, and specially darkened hi-fi and television rooms, where students could play their records or watch television. Everything was tastefully and lavishly appointed. In fact, the whole complex cost several million dollars and represented the very latest in luxury and efficiency. Few students who lived in this new complex could afford to live in similar luxury at home. One can find nothing wrong with this as a straightforward attempt on the part of a wealthy society to provide its future leaders with the very best it can in the way of facilities.

But this is only one side of the picture. The other side, for some, is this: When the student, who has lived for several years in this luxury, graduates, he usually has two paths before him. He either gets his military service out of the way, involved in such horrors as Vietnam (or some other horror of the future), or he may face civilian life. For the earnest Christian the latter may mean becoming a Christian missionary, or a physician, or a teacher.

Military experience. In the case of the military experience, our graduate faces a ruthless, hardened enemy in the steaming jungles (to which the enemy is inured, but to which our graduate is a novice). Or, if he becomes a missionary, physician or teacher he faces with his softened body the pitiless "jungle" in another way. Fresh from the darkened hi-fi rooms at college, he is now living off the jungle, either as a soldier or as a missionary. As such he has to deal with his insect, reptilian and other animal enemies as well as vicious human ones. As a soldier he may see his friends and comrades shot to pieces beside him, or recovered from patrol duty carved up beyond recognition by the enemy. He may see enemy soldiers or even civilians with children burned alive by napalm. He sees helicopters, full of cargo, crash in flames as they spray the enemy with cannon, tear gas or defoliant. Missionaries today must often be prepared to survive in the chaotic conditions of newly emergent nations where bloodshed and anarchy make the mission field another battlefield.

Like child not trained to walk. All this may come as a

colossal shock to any decent, civilized boy brought up by parents and college alike to lead a respectable life in a luxurious setting. The boy's psyche, his mind, has never been stressed or conditioned to take challenge of the kind he is going to get in the years immediately after his graduation, be he soldier, missionary or even modern businessman. In some ways he is like the child who was never allowed to learn to walk, so that his flexors and extensors grew up with too little to allow him to coordinate them, and who is now suddenly thrown to the lions and exhorted to run for his life to avoid being made a meal of. He tries to escape, but he cannot, and he may break down in the effort. This is one explanation of the high percentage of psychical breakdown among juveniles today—and also the high percentage of suicide found in affluent societies such as that of Scandinavia, particularly Sweden.

Protected too long from genuine stress. This, then, is the type of trick being played on so many of the younger members of our society. They are protected too long from genuine stress. Dad will see them through college, maybe through marriage as well, and the first child or two. Then, without having had time to learn to develop their "muscles" by direct and continuous challenge, they are precipitated, like children who have never learned to walk, directly, as it were, into the lion's den. The ordinary child hardens and prepares itself from infancy onward by the process of walking—and falling. After falling it picks itself up as a matter of routine and thus prepares for the harder falls in the real challenge of life. It is *good* for a man to bear the *yoke* in his youth. [7] "Endure hardness, as a good soldier of Jesus Christ," says the Bible. [8] But it is dangerous to catapult today's generation into the jungle of life with only academic learning behind it, even though academic learning is vital in today's technical society.

Another Result of Overprotection

Over and above this danger of "paralysis" when catapulted

without due prestressing before entering the arena of life, the student who is unprepared feels his own insecurity. He has never really "flown" alone and yet feels the urgent need to flex his muscles and his moral fibre. If he cannot begin to do this in college or high school—often there is little opportunity to do this because so much there tends to be "taken care of" for him—then he will most likely be tempted to go in for artificial stimulation or "muscle flexing." It is in this situation that he tries out the "kicks" supplied by sex, drugs, conflict with the police or university authorities, rioting, violence or crime. This is his way of obtaining the challenge he needs. Who can blame him for it? Surely, least of all the affluent society which has been instrumental both in robbing him of his real challenge to exercise his "muscles" and offering him at the same time the financial means of obtaining the drug or other stimuli.

[1] Frank Barron, "Motivational Patterns in LSD Usage," *LSD, Man and Society,* pp. 3-19.
[2] II Cor. 3:17b.
[3] John 8:36.
[4] Lam. 3:27.
[5] Eccles. 3:11.
[6] Heb. 2:15.
[7] Lam. 3:27.
[8] II Tim. 2:3.

12. Dr. Timothy Leary and Psychedelic Drugs

DRUGS REGARDED AS "SACRAMENT"

No examination of the drug scene today would be complete without giving some prominence to Dr. Timothy Leary, dismissed in 1963 from his lectureship in clinical psychology at Harvard University, and now messiah, martyr and high priest of the psychedelic movement. Dr. Leary is very subjective in describing the effects of so-called psychedelic drugs.[1] He calls them, among other terms, a "sacrament," and suggests that marijuana should be used once daily and LSD once weekly. He insists that these drugs enrich human experience, increase creativeness and critical ability and expand human consciousness. Dr. Leary's League for Spiritual Discovery is a practical application of his beliefs.

Seeking Divine Ecstatic Experience

It would be useless and at the same time arrogant to dismiss Dr. Leary as a crackpot of no consequence. At least he has the courage of his convictions and has attracted a large following. He is a highly educated, intelligent man of great humor, who gives the impression of genuinely seeking the divine ecstatic experience. The more educated and serious have diligently sought this experience one way or another in most past human cultures. In fact, it is probably only the present benumbed and anesthetized, stimulus-flooded, materialistically satiated Western society which has shown itself to be indifferent to this religious quest on a scale seldom seen in bygone ages. For our generation—including a large percentage of those who call themselves fundamental, Bible-believing Christians—seems to be largely satisfied with the material vision of power, money, nationalism and pleasure rather than with the beatific vision.

Final Disappointment

These observations do not alter our conviction that Dr. Leary is an advocate of a substitute ecstasy in seeking a purely drug-mediated one. If this is the case (and we think it is) then Dr. Leary's quest will eventually end in disappointment. But he is at least searching diligently, and at considerable personal cost, for an illumination and ecstatic experience about which most Christians either know nothing or do not care to know. The ecstatic divine experience is described within the pages of both the Old and the New Testaments, but obviously the modern form of Christianity with which Dr. Leary is familiar knows nothing of such. Had he been better informed, he might have sought his enlightenment in more orthodox ways. But it is surely partly the responsibility of an effete modern Christianity that Dr. Leary labors under the delusion that Christianity knows nothing of ecstasy but only of the puritanical negation of enjoyment.

Dr. Leary asks,

Where are the laughing Christians? Something twisted grabbed the Christian mind around the third century. Is there any tender mirth left in the cult of the cross? Mystics, prophets, holy men, are all laughers because the religious revelation is a rib-tickling amazement-insight that all human purposes, including your own, are solemn self-deceptions. You see through the game and laugh with God at the cosmic joke. The holy man is the one who can pass on a part of the secret, express the joke, act out a fragment of the riddle. To be a holy man, you have to be a funny man.[2]

Later we will examine the question of the Christian ecstatic experience and compare it with what Dr. Leary offers.

Eastern Religions and Philosophies

Dr. Leary's book *The Politics of Ecstasy* develops various theories on the psychedelic experience which he links with certain Eastern religions and philosophies. He believes it to be a fundamentally religious experience, and transcendental in its outworking. He writes:

The laboratory equipment for experimental theology, for internal science, is of course made of the stuff of consciousness itself, made of the same material as the data to be studied. The instruments of systematic religion are chemicals. Drugs, Dope.... Drugs are the religion of the twenty-first century. Pursuing the religious life of today without using psychedelic drugs is like studying astronomy with the naked eye because that's how they did it in the first century A.D., and besides, telescopes are unnatural.[3]

Dr. Leary's League for Spiritual Discovery does not regard LSD primarily as a means of producing "kicks" but rather as a sacrament to be compared with the Roman Catholic Host.[4] Of course, if one regards a "flirtation with God," as Dr. Leary calls the psychedelic experience, as a "kick," then one may perhaps be entitled to regard the word "kick" as appropriate. Ecstasy may then be regarded as a real "kick"! But in this case all religion should contain an ecstatic element and afford a "kick." This element is certainly conspicuous by its absence in a large section of Christendom today.

Dr. Leary's personal religion is Hinduism.[5] He has spent some time in India and has obviously absorbed a great deal of Eastern mysticism. Since present Western Christianity contains little of the vital ecstasy Dr. Leary has found both in

264

drugs and in Eastern mysticism, it is not surprising that he and his movement hold little respect for the Christianity influencing most of American culture at present.

Ancient Man Closer to Divinity

It is Dr. Leary's thesis that centuries ago, man and society were so much healthier than they are at present, that contact with the divinity in man in the ecstatic state was much more easily reached than it is in our day and age. According to him, in early times man could, with great facility, change his consciousness and turn on by the various means at his disposal—such as breathing exercises, fasting, flagellation, dancing, solitude or diet.[6]

> But at the present time man is so sick that there are very few people who can use these ancient methods, so that today it is safe to say that drugs are the specific and almost the only way that the American is ever going to have a religious experience.[7]
>
> The genetic code is infinite in its variation and wisdom and always comes out with the right answer; and exactly the right answer for the particular neurological disease that man has been plagued by for the last 1000 years is LSD. You see, 3000 or 4000 years ago, LSD wouldn't have been necessary. Man was in touch. He was harmoniously dancing along with the change in the planets, the change in the seasons. He was in touch, he was in tune, he was turned on. LSD existed in natural form. LSD has been in morning glory seeds for hundreds of thousands of years. But until now it hasn't been necessary to use because you wouldn't have had to have the effect. [8]

There is considerable evidence, of course, that ancient man was, as Dr. Leary maintains, far more "in touch" with the transcendent and with divinity than modern man. There is also plenty of evidence that modern man with his hurry and technology is directly antagonistic to transcendence or mysticism of any sort. For the effect of modern man on the Christian way of life has been approximately the same as his effect on the Eastern religions. Many missionaries are of the opinion that the old Japanese faiths are wilting under modern technology in the same way that ancient tribal beliefs are dying out in Africa and the South Sea Islands. For modern technology is putting man out of touch with transcendence in general, be it good or bad. Simple stimulus-flooding, due to the communications explosion, may be partly at the bottom of this, as we have already pointed out.

DR. LEARY AND AMERICAN (WESTERN) CULTURE

Following this line of thought, Dr. Leary never ceases to emphasize the futility and insanity of Western and particularly American culture. He points out the utter ineffectiveness of even fundamental Christian views in making headway in the milieu of this kind of culture, which is inimical to any belief in the transcendent. This brings us to the question of Leary's view of American and Western culture in general.

Seen as Insane Asylum

Innisfree, the monthly journal of inquiry published by students at the Massachusetts Institute of Technology, interviewed Dr. Leary and asked him various questions, including this: "You don't feel that LSD culture is compatible with American culture now, then?"

Leary answered,

> I don't think the American culture is compatible with anything. Certainly not with anything that's been going on in this planet since the origin of life. The American culture is an insane asylum. You take for granted such things as race prejudice, the Protestant work culture, the professional bureaucracy which exists in this country, the complete loss of euphoria which has developed in the past fifty years. Dropping bombs on the natives of Vietnam—well, that's just like a head cold. I mean, that's the way it's supposed to be. It's the current symptom of our insanity. LSD and the LSD cult is perfectly in tune with the wisdom of the Buddha or the great philosophies of the past. The Buddha could walk up this road to our house here at Millbrook, and he'd see the signs of his profession because we belong to the

> same profession, people who are changing consciousness,
> who are pursuing the eternal quest. [9]

Conforms with Christianity

Although this indictment of society may appear to many
to be severe, yet it is, in essence, in conformity with the
biblical Christian view of man in general. Man's lack of
interest in the Divine, and his absorbing concern with power,
possession and his own ego, show him to be lost and,
therefore—because he has found no divine redeemer—
damned. Surely the fact that he himself uses most of his great
inventions to destroy himself, proves his factual damnation.
Consider the atomic and hydrogen bombs. So hopelessly
insane is man and his society, at least in the biblical view,
that the apostles taught us that even to love the world and its
system was equivalent to hating God. [10] The same source
instructs us that the Christian's main job during his lifetime
is to save individuals from being enmeshed in this world, its
goods and philosophies. [11] As many individuals as possible
are to be saved from the fire of judgment which awaits a
willfully corrupt and disobedient society. The marvel of it all
is that Dr. Leary sees the human corruption and insanity,
tries to persuade the young to drop out of this mad society,
and yet says not a word about the punishment (a forbidden
word today) which must await willful destructive attitudes to
all that is divine and good. Here is the big hole in his
philosophy; thus, biblical philosophies and doctrines are
certainly superior to those of Dr. Leary.

On the other hand, there are many points of congruence
between the biblical and the psychedelic views. The Christian
is, for example, to act as salt does in preserving food from
corruption. [12] Society in general is putrefying in both views.
Dr. Leary wishes his turned-on people to "tune in" and win
others from the putrefying society about them, so that they,
too, can experience the ecstasy of being in touch with the
divine reality.

Thus, the evangelical Christian would do well to admit that

he shares at least some of Dr. Leary's views on certain aspects of modern society. He can certainly share Dr. Leary's admonitions to have no part in resistance or rebellion against authority but to bear restrictions with patience, good humor and love. Apparently Dr. Leary was able to win the two federal agents who "busted" him at Laredo, Texas, for these two agents were present and on friendly terms with him at one of his news conferences.[13]

Why Are Christians Blind?

How is it, then, that the psychedelics see the true state of society more clearly than many Christians? Surely not because these matters are not taught clearly enough in the Bible. May it not be that Christians are implicated in the same covetousness, lust for power and prestige, and general materialism which motivates decaying society around them? In this way Christians may recognize these dangers with their minds but not with their wills and hearts. For if they did, would they not adopt a somewhat similar attitude to that of psychedelics toward many aspects of their relationship to society and the state? As things stand, one often cannot distinguish between a convinced member of the sick society (i.e., a worldling) and a so-called Christian.

Is it then any wonder that the younger generation, which already has a built-in tendency to rebel against the Establishment, has gotten the message from Dr. Leary and to a large extent turned its back on Christianity? To some extent Dr. Leary has brought them a message which they needed. They needed to recognize society for what it really is, so that they could escape its snares in their search to satisfy their hunger for the transcendent. Recognizing society for what it is constitutes the first necessity in supplying the missionary spirit. And Dr. Leary's followers certainly have this spirit.

DR. LEARY'S MANIFESTO

Under the title of *Neurological Politics* Dr. Leary has published a manifesto in the following terms:

268

> We, therefore, God-loving, life-loving, fun-loving men and
> women, appealing to the Supreme Judge of the Universe for
> the rectitude of our intentions, do, in the name and by the
> Authority of all sentient beings who seek gently to evolve
> on this planet, solemnly publish and declare that we are
> free and independent, and that we are absolved from all
> Allegiance to the United States Government and all
> governments controlled by the menopausal, and that
> grouping ourselves into tribes of like-minded fellows we
> claim full power to live and move on the land, obtain
> sustenance with our own hands and minds in the style
> which seems sacred and holy to us, and to do all Acts and
> Things which independent Freemen and Freewomen may
> of right do without infringing on the same rights of other
> species and groups to do their own thing.[14]

On viewing this declaration, the only point a Christian might like to add would be an assurance that the believer would "render unto Caesar the things that are Caesar's and unto God the things that are God's." Everyone must interpret this, the wisdom of the Lord Jesus Christ, according to the biblical view of what is God's and what is Caesar's. One of the duties of Caesar is to punish evildoers and reward welldoers.[15] For this and other duties Caesar has the right to collect taxes, but otherwise the Christian is responsible to God for his actions. But Caesar, the state, is failing grievously in the God-appointed duties and in his raison d'être if he does not maintain order and justice in the area under his control. If he is incompetent here he is likely to be incompetent in other fields of responsibility too.

HOW TO TRANSFORM MEN

Demanding Message

This brings us to the largely futile efforts on the part of Christians to reach and convert the younger generation. Dr. Leary can and has reached this generation with a very demanding message—that of dropping out of their soft jobs, abandoning their avarice and forsaking the rat race. Years ago people such as Moody, Sankey, George Müller, Wesley, Whitefield and others possessed a similar hold over their generation with an analogous message. Thousands changed their life ambitions and gave up good jobs to go to the uttermost parts of the earth, often amid great hardship, for the sake of the gospel in which they believed. Today, if one can persuade a young Christian to go at all, he too often insists on taking his comforts with him!

Dr. Leary clearly states his views on this matter.

> Gautama's question is exactly that anguishing dilemma faced by several million young Americans who have taken psychedelic trips in the last five years. Because, when seen *sub specie aeternitatis,* American society really does appear quite destructive and insane. What can LBJ or Billy Graham offer a dropped-out, turned-on, ill-prepared, confused teen-ager visionary? [16]

Because most Christians show little transformation and do not draw the line of inward, spiritual separation from surrounding society, Dr. Leary significantly puts them in the same class as the welfare programs of today's politicians.

To Change Men and Women for the Better

Yet the goal of transcendent, mystical ecstasy is to bring the tripper into a new relationship to God and the realms to which they were previously dead. It is also intended to change men and women, and to change them for the better:

> I would say that at present our society is so insane, that even if the risks were fifty-fifty that if you took LSD you would be permanently insane, I still think that the risk is worth taking, as long as the person knows that that's the risk. There is a complete breakdown in assumption here. You're operating from a psychiatric metaphor, and I'm operating from a religious metaphor. I say that the confrontation with divinity is going to change you, and there are some people who are in such a state of sin that they don't want to confront divinity; they freak out. Such people should be warned that if you come into this temple

you're going to face blazing illumination of the divinity. It's going to change you completely; you're never going to be the same. [17]

It's very hard work to change the human psychology, even with LSD. That should give comfort to the frightened, and probably anguish to the optimistic like myself.[18]

Change During His Lifetime

Dr. Leary is optimistic enough to believe that this fundamental change in man's nature can take place during his lifetime. He maintains that this change threatens the establishment and is therefore frowned upon by it:

The game between those who know that man can change and become divine in his lifetime [Christians, remember the promise that the Christian after his rebirth obtains Christ's mind (I Cor. 2:16)!] and want to teach people how to do it, completely threatens the establishment. In every generation you say: "No, it's all been done and settled, and just get your lawyer-priest and do what we tell you to do." And this dialogue between the establishment and the utopian visionaries will inevitably exist in every historical era. [19]

The Christian also believes that man is capable of change. For the Bible teaches that the transcendent contemplation of Christ will transform him by stages into a likeness of Christ during his lifetime here on earth: "And we all, with unveiled face, beholding the glory of the Lord, are being changed into his likeness from one degree of glory to another; for this comes from the Lord who is the Spirit." [20]

It is thus perfectly clear that the Christian shares Dr. Leary's optimism that man can change, even though the process may be extremely difficult. The Christian also believes that the change is divine—man is destined to change into the likeness of the Divinity by means of the illumination he finds in Christ.

OPPOSITION IS HELPFUL

Dr. Leary then goes on to show how opposition very often

helps rather than hinders the cause which is opposed:

> The fact that they [the authorities of the Establishment] want to hound me out of existence is right. They should, just like the Harvard defensive team wants to throw offensive's quarterback for a loss. I have no complaint about this; I'm perfectly good-humored about it. The more energy that is directed against me, the more energy is available for me. It's the perfect physical law of jujitsu—the more government and professional establishment dynamism that is set off against what we're doing is just a sign to us that we're doing fine. [21]

One wonders if this observation of Dr. Leary might not explain some at least of the lack of energy and dynamism characterizing so much Christian effort. Indeed, "all who desire to live a godly life in Christ Jesus will be persecuted"[22] would seem, seen in this light, to be a guarantee of power and success in missionary activity! And might not a lack of persecution mean that a godly life in Christ Jesus was not being consistently lived? Not that persecution should be experienced all the time; even in the case of the Lord's life on earth this was not the case. But times of persecution must be experienced sometime by all who are godly and all who seek the beatific vision.

THE MEANING OF THE TERM "DROPOUT"

Dr. Leary's slogan is "Turn on, tune in and drop out." He is very careful to explain that dropping out does not merely mean dropping out of school or quitting one's job:

> I want to be very clear about the term "drop out." I don't mean external dropping out. I certainly don't mean acts of rebellion or irresponsibility to any social situation you are involved in. But I urge any of you who are serious about life, who are serious about your nervous system or your spiritual future, to start right now planning how you can harmoniously, sequentially, lovingly and gracefully detach yourself from the social commitments to which you are addicted. . . . Another thing you can do is to be careful

> with whom you spend your time. . . . The more I study the neurology of the psychedelic experience, the more awed and amazed I am at what we can do with and to each other's nervous systems. [23]

What sounder advice could one Christian offer to another? It is the fashion today to advise young Christians to "get involved in social commitments." While the intention may be good, the practice is against the warnings of Scripture against getting entangled (i.e., "addicted to") in such commitments: "No soldier on service gets entangled in civilian pursuits, since his aim is to satisfy the one who enlisted him."[24] Anything that encumbers the freedom of the one who is going to war is to be rejected.

DR. LEARY'S VIEWS ON THE MEANING AND PURPOSE OF LIFE

Regarded as Strictly Religious

Consistent with the rest of his views on psychedelic drugs, Dr. Leary regards the purpose of life as strictly religious:

> Every human being is born divine and . . . the purpose of life is to rediscover your forgotten divinity. [25]
>
> Like it or not, or believe it or not, I'm convinced that the religious kick is the only experience that makes life worthwhile. The moment of revelation when you're turned on to the whole process, which men of old called the mystic, is the whole purpose of life. . . . All the concepts about virtue, hard work, and being good are part of that old con game. Religion to us is ecstasy. It is freedom and harmony. Kids should not let the fake, television-prop religion turn them off. The real trip is the God trip. [26]

Here the hedonistic nature of Dr. Leary's religion comes out. The old mystics experienced the beatific vision as a result of a life of good works, self-denial, solitude, prayer and fasting. They were saints in the ordinary sense of the word and experienced quite naturally the vision of a saint. Dr. Leary has introduced the concept of "biochemical mysticism" which can be experienced by "saint or sinner," good or bad, as long as he is in a position to obtain the necessary drugs, place himself in the correct surroundings under a reliable guide, and does not possess psychotic tendencies in his makeup.

"You will find it absolutely necessary to leave the city. Urban living is spiritually suicidal. . . . Go to the land. Go to the sea. . . . There they form their clans. They migrate from the city." [27] Here again the necessity of a correct setting for the outworking of the religious aspects of psychedelic drugs is emphasized. Dr. Leary is harking back to the attitude of the solitary mystic. The great difference is that he uses drugs instead of asceticism to achieve his ends.

> Remember, your body is the kingdom of heaven, and your home is the shrine in which the kingdom of heaven is to be found. . . . If you take a psychedelic sacrament, leave your house and commit a disorder on Caesar's streets, let him arrest you for overt crime. But your right to turn on in your own home is sacred. You make your home a shrine by writing it into the charter of your religion. [28]

> The key concept of the psychedelic revolution is work—ecstatic work. This central point is missed by enthusiastic acidheads as well as horrified burghers. Each deluded the other with the notion of escape and naughty pleasure. [29]

Main Purpose of Drugs Is Ecstasy

In Dr. Leary's view, the main emphasis of the psychedelic drug revolution has nothing to do with escapism or even with the kicks of illicit pleasure. The main purpose lies in the purely religious sphere—religious, hedonistic ecstasy. As Dr. Leary says, this is natural, since neither our present sick society nor its religion know anything of religious euphoria—and man needs euphoria. Thus a substitute for man's need for religious euphoria must be provided and is, in fact, found in psychedelic euphoria.

"We declare the identity of flesh and consciousness." [30] Elsewhere Dr. Leary declares that DNA is the soul of man, [31] which shows that he believes the mind and body of man to be identical. This is why, in his view, biochemicals change the soul and mind of man. The drugs are physical agents controlling a physically framed soul—the DNA molecule.

> It is of interest that the heroin addict and the illuminated Buddha end up at the same place. The void. The junkie is a deeply religious person. The alcoholic is, too. Thus our physicians and psychiatrists have no luck in "curing" addicts. If you see an addict as a social misfit, a civic nuisance who must be rehabilitated, you completely miss the point. To cure the junkie and the alcoholic, you must humbly admit that he is a more deeply spiritual person than you. [32]
>
> LSD is Western Yoga. The aim of all Eastern religion, like the aim of LSD, is basically to get high: that is, to expand your consciousness and find ecstasy and revelation within. [33]

THE CHRISTIAN VIEW OF ECSTASY AND EUPHORIA

What is the Christian view of ecstasy and euphoria? By the Christian view we mean, of course, the teaching set out in the Christian Scriptures, though not necessarily taught by so-called Christian denominations which have, in some cases, long since abandoned the original biblical positions of their founders.

The history of the growing "tongues" movement is clear evidence of man's need and desire for ecstatic experience, whether or not we agree with the doctrinal emphasis behind this movement.

Scriptures Teach Euphoria

It must surely be clear to the unbiased that the Scriptures teach euphoria as a fundamental part of the basic message: "Rejoice in Christ Jesus." [34] "Believe in him and rejoice with unutterable and exalted joy." [35] "Rejoice, and be exceeding glad." [36] "We will rejoice in thy salvation." [37] "In the shadow of thy wings will I rejoice." [38] One has only to look up the word "rejoice" in a concordance to see that both the Old and the New Testaments are full of euphoria of this type. But it is also equally clear that the actual message transmitted by the church to the outside world today does not savor much of real euphoria. If a basic need of mankind is religious euphoria, as Dr. Leary obviously believes, then this need is by and large not being met by the Christian church. "Where are the laughing Christians?" Thus, it is scarcely surprising that if the pastures within the church are not green enough, especially for the younger, euphoria-hungry generation, then this generation will look elsewhere to satisfy its hunger. The psychedelic movement is meeting this need, even if it is meeting it with a substitute.

Apostles' Ecstatic Experiences

Many critics of the Christian message, among them Dr. Leary, do not seem to realize that the Bible teaches ecstasy, even that reaching up to out-of-the-body experience of a type even more transforming than that known to the psychedelics. The revelation given by God to the Apostle John was surely an ecstatic and transcendental experience. And Paul the Apostle describes what happened to him:

> I must boast; there is nothing to be gained by it, but I will go on to visions and revelations of the Lord. I know a man in Christ who fourteen years ago was caught up to the third heaven—whether in the body or out of the body I do not know, God knows. And I know that this man was caught up into Paradise—whether in the body or out of the body I do not know, God knows—and he heard things that cannot be told, which man may not utter.[39]

Obviously the great apostle was what Dr. Leary would call "out of his mind" in that ecstatic experience. The apostle was not permitted to report on what he had actually experienced—or he could not find words to do so—except that it was an experience of heaven and paradise. Dr. Leary himself says that words are often a poor medium to transmit the ecstatic experience.

While it is obvious that such ecstatic experiences were rare even in the life of the apostle—to say nothing of the ecstasy-deprived society in which we live today—yet ecstasy was a part of his message. It was in this state that he received various revelations from the Lord, and he says so. We are apt to forget that "alleluia" is an integral part of the biblical message.

Man's Great Need for Euphoria

Obviously God gave us this message of euphoria and ecstasy—first, because it was a part of his message, and second, because we need it. If now the Christian church suppresses or does not recognize this part of his message (How can it? It knows so little of it.), then we should not be surprised if God allows others to bring the message and meet man's basic need for it. Nor should we be surprised if some counterfeiting goes on, seeing the need is so great in all sections of mankind.

God tells us that in his presence is fullness of joy and ecstasies everlasting,[40] so we scarcely need to be told that this is one of the basic built-in needs we must have satisfied. If biochemical mysticism meets even part of this need in a society starved of euphoria and ecstasy, is it to be wondered that stolid Evangelicals and denominationalists stand helplessly by and watch the stampede to the new psychedelic fountains of joy? A primary cause of the stampede lies in the choking thirst produced by generations of religion devoid of true joy. It is no use forbidding biochemical ecstasy. The cure is for those who possess the dried-up fountains to allow them to well up again.

Orthodox Christianity can learn from biochemical mysticism what has been lacking in its own Christian message. We have been one-sided in our presentation and experience of the gospel. The success of the psychedelic movement has shown us a basic need of man which we had not guessed at before, but which is well covered by the basic Christian message if we would only see it. The success of Dr. Leary's message of ecstasy, instead of being an unmitigated threat, puts the Christian church on the spot and, in a very pointed manner, shows its own failure. It also reveals where repentance and a change of attitude are urgently needed. To reject this sign of the times is to refuse to learn—and to refuse to serve our generation. Dr. Leary's message and its reception by the younger generation shows how much we Christians have muffed our message and missed the real experience of things transcendent.

[1] See Timothy Leary, *The Politics of Ecstasy*.
[2] *Ibid.*, p. 321.
[3] *Ibid.*, p. 44.
[4] *Ibid.*, p. 297.
[5] *Ibid.*, pp. 157, 293.
[6] *Ibid.*, p. 297.
[7] *Ibid.*
[8] *Ibid.*, pp. 295-96.
[9] *Ibid.*, p. 296.
[10] James 4:4.
[11] Jude 23.
[12] Matt. 5:13; Mark 9:50; Col. 4:6.
[13] Leary, p. 337.
[14] *Ibid.*, pp. 362-65.
[15] Matt. 22:21; Mark 12:17; Luke 20:25, I Peter 2:13-14.
[16] Leary, p. 307.
[17] *Ibid.*, pp. 299-300.
[18] *Ibid.*, p. 301.
[19] *Ibid.*, p. 302.
[20] II Cor. 3:18.
[21] Leary, *ibid.*
[22] II Tim. 3:12 (RSV).
[23] Leary, pp. 358-59.
[24] II Tim. 2:4 (RSV).
[25] Leary, p. 369.
[26] *Ibid.*, p. 274.
[27] *Ibid.*, p. 232.
[28] *Ibid.*, p. 233.
[29] *Ibid.*, p. 347.
[30] *Ibid.*, p. 371.
[31] *Ibid.*, pp. 94, 220.
[32] *Ibid.*, p. 43.
[33] *Ibid.*, p. 135.
[34] Phil. 3:3.
[35] I Peter 1:8 (RSV).
[36] Matt. 5:12.
[37] Ps. 20:5a.
[38] Ps. 63:7b.
[39] II Cor. 12:1-4 (RSV).
[40] Ps. 16:11; cf. Neh. 8:10.

13. The Implications of Hallucinogenic Drugs

We have already described the kind of torpor or anesthesia which seems to have settled down on modern society and which would appear to arise at least in part from the phenomenon known as stimulus flooding. This benumbing comes over an individual when he is exposed to more sensory input than he can cope with in the decoding centers of the brain. In this state of lethargy or anesthesia the member of the affluent society is different from his forefathers, who were, perhaps rather under- than over-stimulated. They were, therefore, perhaps wakeful and suspicious rather than sleepy, socially speaking.

Skin Must Be Thickened

As a result of this stimulus flooding, these multitudinous stimuli which reach our sensory perceptors every minute of the day, the ordinary member of the affluent society has been forced to "thicken his skin," that is, he is forced to ignore a percentage of the calls constantly made for his attention. In order to survive he has been obliged to delegate more and more of his own proper interests to other people to look after. This is particularly the case in socialist and secularized states and societies, with the not unnatural result that the ordinary citizen comes to lean on others to have his needs met in certain areas, rather than on his own efforts. The more uniformly organized society becomes, the more widespread becomes the conviction that society, the community or the company which employs me will look after "all that." It is a very short step from this position to that where the individual comes to believe that individual effort is worthless anyway and only the whole team counts. Only the team can cope in the very nature of complex society. Thus the value of the individual as an individual is already beginning to be eroded.

DEPENDENCE ON PILLS

Coupled with the above idea runs the notion, present at least unconsciously in many people's thinking today, that there is "a pill for everything." If one has a headache, one takes aspirin. If one is suffering from an infection, then an immediate dose of the correct antibiotic is indicated. If one does not want any children, one can always take a contraceptive pill. But where does the use of pills end and their abuse start? It is not always advisable to take an antibiotic on the very first signs of infection; it is sometimes better to wait a while. For if one waits while the infection is brewing, the body will have time to build up its own immunity toward the infecting organism. In this case the premature use of an antibiotic may constitute an abuse of the drug. Similar considerations apply in the use of contraceptive pills. A little dose of self-discipline would render many doses of this type of artificial protection superfluous. Self-discipline would tone up the moral fibre and character of the marriage partners and lead to the phenomenon of psychological sublimation of the sex drive which may then be directed toward creative activity in other areas. The tendency today is to partake of and exploit to the maximum any and every pleasure offered to man. The result is, that instead of saying no to himself and so developing a tension or pressure within his psyche, modern man says yes to every pleasure, so letting off his "steam" or "pressure," which leaves him at the end of the day a flabby mass which has given in to every pleasure offered. The tension being expended, there is little left to devote to higher artistic or other noble ends.

Thus we have two ideas to consider. The first is that most things can be delegated from the individual to the "team"— represented by society or even the state. The second is that there is a "pill for everything," which leads to drug abuse. Both ideas tend to erode personal responsibility—to disarm the individual in favor of the mass, or medicaments. This is not to belittle the idea of the team which a man may altruistically serve with profit. The situation which we need to avoid is that which leads the individual to shirk his duties because the team or medicaments will take care of everything. It is the shirking of personal, individual responsibility which is the plague today in all aspects of society. It is usually coupled with the lethargy we have noted already which in some cases may have its origin in the ubiquitous stimulus flooding to which society subjects us, and which leads to a kind of tired fatalism, which seems to be incapable of taking up any personal challenge, even when it is offered.

The early Christians in the Near East and in Europe were not in the least fatalistic. A brief study of the Acts of the Apostles will convince any open mind of that fact. They gladly took the heaviest forms of responsibility and challenge upon themselves and their families for the gospel's sake. They actively, not fatalistically, relied on God's support for the ability to carry out their divine commission. And wherever their commission penetrated we find ordinary people becoming like the apostles and being fired with the same zeal, warmth and energy to take up personal challenge.

REFORMATIONS AND REVIVALS

After Luther's Reformation in Europe, the same tendency which we have noted in the Acts occurred all over again. Men and women began to search out and accept personal challenge. Less and less "buck passing" took place, the more the Reformation and its doctrines spread. The net result was that Christian people the world over became more prosperous personally and more effective in their communities. The sense of personal responsibility in matters of salvation and of business helped to overcome a certain human fatalism which often manifests itself in priestly caste systems (Catholic or Protestant, with the priest vicariously bearing the responsibility for the salvation of the individual and the nation, thus taking this responsibility out of their hands). In the Reformation and later, the effective priesthood of all believers was reemphasized so that all who believed came to realize the vital personal responsibility involved in the faith they professed. This was a heavy and decisive blow at human fatalism and irresponsibility.

This same tendency was emphatically seen in the Wesleyan and Whitefield revivals of two centuries ago. By becoming active, devout and hard-working as a result of faith in God, rather than lazily relying on the priest or the other member of the team, the Methodist or the follower of George Whitefield generally became a successful and fulfilled individual. It appears, therefore, that the early Christians, the followers of Luther and the other Reformers, together with the disciples of the later reformations under Wesley and Whitefield, were genuinely influenced by their doctrines to accept personal challenge as from their God. In accepting this personal challenge they experienced real achievement and personal fulfillment.

This is in no way to be interpreted as a deprecation of dedicated priests or theologians. On the contrary, some of the most dedicated and intelligent people I know and whom I count as my firm friends, are priests. They have accepted the personal challenge of God in taking up their profession (and their cross daily) as a step of obedience toward the divine call. But the above considerations still remain realities in past and present society.

TODAY'S APATHETIC CHURCH

The church today is apathetic. This is a very general observation. Its corollary is also true. For, in general, as a society falls away from a living, personal faith in God, it tends to become increasingly apathetic, fatalistic and given to irresponsibility. In addition, Christians today in spite of modern revivals of religion, seem to be characterized by the absence or near absence of the sense of personal challenge and responsibility to do God's will every hour of their human existence—a trait which marked participants in all the older revivals. Petty dishonesties may be tolerated. Laziness at work may pass as a matter of course. The use of unclean language and swearing is not uncommon. Marital troubles and even divorce openly take place even in conservative churches without much eyebrow-raising. With regard to clothing and modesty, fashion rather than the Bible's standards decides how women dress to come to church. The use of cosmetics sometimes rivals the standards set up by Jezebel centuries ago. In fact, apart from certain rather high-sounding "statements of faith," it is often most difficult to pick out the modern believer among the unbelievers in the affluent society. The conformity of Christians to the world's standards render them almost indistinguishable. Why is this so?

THE BIBLICAL BALANCE OF FAITH AND WORKS

The apostles, the early Christian Fathers, Luther, Whitefield, Wesley and many others were careful to teach what the Bible calls justification by faith. That is, that a man is not justified by his works. He cannot buy off the consequences of his wrongdoing by trying to balance his bad works by the weight (if any) of his good works. The weight of bad works is so overwhelming in us all that no weight of good will ever balance things again. The Bible and all who stick to it, teach that a man is justified by faith in the Son of God who died to balance things.

Easy to Profess Faith

Now, it is not so very difficult to profess that one has faith in the Son of God. Words are easier to pronounce than to put in practice. Thus, a criterion of faith is needed to ascertain whether the faith a man possesses is what is called "saving faith" or whether it is only "vain faith." For there are the two kinds of faith—the "saving type" which makes a man a devout Christian, or the "vain faith" in which the devils indulge when they believe (have faith) in God and tremble, but which does not bring them to repentance nor to saving faith.

Faith Void Without Works

The Bible teaches that faith is void unless it produces in a man works like those which God's Son practiced in obtaining our redemption. For he gave himself, he sacrificed himself, he died to attain our redemption. If a man possesses saving faith he will show the same attitude of mind in saying no to himself as Christ did. This does not mean that a man's works will redeem him, but it does mean that a man will have so placed his trust in Christ that he will adopt Christ's attitude toward life and mankind. Such a man will also adopt Christ's attitude of self-discipline and self-denial in reaching men. To put it in the old language, to be Christ's disciples we must be willing to take up our cross daily and follow him. If a man really believes in Christ's redeeming work he will start to do the same kind of work that Christ did, for he will have learned to love Christ's way of life and his attitude to it. That is, true trust in Christ, when exercised by a man, will convert that man in the course of time to a sort of rough model of Christ (a working model, if you wish) in whom he believes, and whom he sincerely believes to be right in his attitude to life and its problems. It will be a poor model of Christ, man being what he is, but a resemblance in principle will be there.

Transforming Work Begins at Once

The apostles, the Reformers and others went a step further in maintaining that, if a man becomes a Christian, this transforming work of changing him into a resemblance of Christ will start at once, simultaneously with his conversion. His works will begin to correspond to his faith. The two processes—works and faith—are inextricably interwoven and can never be separated. For the one gives rise to the other and the second is the expression of the first.

In summary, the Christian way of life has two aspects. The first and most important aspect is that the Son of God gave himself in death to effect the basis for the redemption of humanity. The second aspect is that, if this redemptive act is to bear any fruit in humanity, then it will do so immediately as humanity begins to give itself into death to itself in the same way as Christ gave himself for it.

CHRIST AND THE BELIEVER—A BALANCED RELATIONSHIP

Perfect Example of Tonus

Thus we have here a perfect example of the tonus, or tension, we have been discussing, the metaphorical interplay between flexor and the extensor systems. The one pull must maintain itself against the other, both in the muscle systems we have looked into and in the relationship between Christ and humanity. The Apostle Paul expressed this in the following way: Christ by his love to Paul "apprehended" Paul—won him. Such a Character and Person as Christ "gained" Paul's entire confidence when the two met on the Damascus road. This winning of Paul by Christ had one immediate effect. The apostle resolved in his heart that just as Christ has "won" his confidence so he, the apostle, was now going to set out for the rest of his life to "win" Christ's confidence toward himself, to "win" Christ![1] The apostle was by no means trying to buy his salvation by his technique.

Rather, out of thankfulness for the redemption which Christ had won him at so great a cost, he was signifying that from then on he was going to bend all his efforts to return to Christ, by his works and by his life, the love that Christ had shown him.

Both Must Give Their All

The apostle's efforts were, of course, puny compared with those of Christ for the apostle. But the works of Christ and of the apostle had one factor in common. Christ gave his all—his very life itself—for us, of his own free will, according to the testimony of Scripture. Therefore, the apostle had to respond with a similar freewill gift. He too had to give his all. Paul's all, was, of course, infinitely less than the "all" offered by the Son of God. But not even God can demand more than a man has to give!

Thus, my "all" is just enough to meet Christ's "all" in the flexor-extensor relationship between Christ and me, his redeemed. Only on the basis of this total balance between flexor action and extensor action is "muscular health" possible for Christians. Without this balanced relationship between Christ and his redeemed, various kinds of "muscular dystrophy" leading to impotence in Christian life will become evident. Because any kind of life or faith that does not aim at a total balancing of the love relationship between the Redeemer and the redeemed is not the kind of life or faith of which the Bible speaks.

CHRISTIANITY'S ROLE IN TODAY'S SOCIETY

These considerations now put us in a position to return to one of our main problems. Has Christianity played any role in maneuvering Western society into its present impasse, characterized by violence, drug epidemics and anarchy, particularly in intellectual and student circles?

Basic truth known. Today, especially in the United States, one side of the Christian gospel has been, generally speaking, well emphasized and preached. It is that God gave his Son to redeem humanity from its sin. Few must be the citizens of the United States or Canada who have never heard this truth. A large percentage of the ordinary GI's I contacted during World War II knew this basic fact of Christian truth.

Humanity's part less well known. It is the equally important necessity of a total response on the part of humanity to Christ's love, in short, the "flexor-extensor relationship," which is much less well known. That Christ responded to me is well known. The necessity of my responding to him is less well known. In fact, this tendency in Christian circles to divide these two "pulls" into separate entities represents one of the real dangers to the Christian message as taught today. For there is a definite tendency to divide "becoming saved" from "becoming holy" and to treat the two experiences as separate ones. It should by now be obvious that any attempt to isolate the flexor from the extensor or to regard the extensor as independent of the flexor will merely result in destruction of the whole "tonus" of the system. A Christian must be totally involved in the "push and pull" to an equal and balanced degree. This total "tone" is known in the Scriptures as holiness. But neither "pull" can ever be regarded as a separate entity.

Think Faith Is Enough

It has generally been taught, particularly in some forms of Christianity associated with Western affluent society, that faith without works will save a man. As long as he confesses Christ and says he trusts him, that man's eternal security is regarded as guaranteed and should not be questioned. It is just here that the cause of some of the present troubles afflicting "affluent Christendom" may arise.

The belief that faith alone, without works, saves a man may be correct from a purely theological and intellectual point of view. But it is certainly incorrect from a dynamic biblical point of view. For the works of faith cannot be separated from the faith that causes them, and a faith that produces no biblical works is not a saving faith. Men respond to the attraction of Christ by accepting his work of salvation completed for them at Calvary. At the same time they respond to this attraction, not only by accepting the gift of salvation but by setting out to attract Christ's confidence in them, that is, by winning him.[2] Here again we come to the inescapable and inseparable flexor-extensor relationships between Christ and the Christian. The attempt by preachers to separate salvation from the works accompanying salvation has resulted in a Christianity whose ways are almost indistinguishable from those of the world from which it was supposed to have been saved by Christ's blood. Thus to be a Christian may mean very little today, for it does not seem to matter if one's ways do not change much when one becomes a Christian.

Holy Spirit limited. The consequence of this development is that God's Holy Spirit cannot do his mighty works in a worldly Christian, so that Christianity becomes flabby, weak and languid. The Scriptures warn us clearly enough that to love the world, to be lukewarm or flabby, is to hate God. The admonition is to be transformed by the renewing of one's mind and not to be conformed to the ways of his lost world.[3] For conformity follows from an impotent gospel. An impotent gospel is one which has cut the extensor-flexor relationship with the result that the so-called body (of Christ) has become paralyzed.

MARRIAGE—A FURTHER ILLUSTRATION

Totality on both sides. The real marriage relationship will illustrate totality and absolute exclusiveness on both sides, the total pull of the one husband being met by the total pull of the one wife. Anything less on both sides is a rupture or an unbalancing of marital flexor and extensor tone. The result of this equilibrium is mutual health of "marital muscle"—a strong, stable, firm husband-wife relationship capable of withstanding the stress of life, particularly of marital life and the bringing up of children. But if there is weakness or unbalancing in either of the partners, anything less than total, happy, convinced, exclusive abandonment one to the other, then the tone is upset. Lopsidedness is followed by weakening of the mutual challenge, resulting in "muscle degeneration" in the marriage relationship.

Both Must Actively Serve and Love

One further analysis is necessary. If one partner in the marital equilibrium allows himself or herself to be actively served or loved more than he or she loves or serves, then trouble is brewing. If one partner does all the serving while the other just sits still and "basks" in the love and service of the other, without being spurred on to do likewise, then an imbalance will again occur and the abandon of love in the marital relationship will be dampened. As both partners serve each other and bear with each other in the various vicissitudes which visit all marriages, health and vitality are maintained in the partnership.

Christian Cannot Be Idle

This is the basic point which is often forgotten in marital and other relationships, as well as in the Christian's relationship to Christ. It is an impossibility for the Christian to onesidedly "bask in the expression of God's love to him in Christ" if he does not equally assiduously seek to allow Christ to "bask in the expression of his love to him." This may, at first, sound remarkable, but the idea is certainly within the spirit of the New Testament, which informs us that God seeks his pleasure among the sons of men.[4] As God seeks to gain our confidence by becoming our Redeemer, so the redeemed individuals must seek to gain the Redeemer's confidence by becoming his servants and disciples. But he gains us and our confidence by sacrifice (the cross) just as we gain him and his confidence by sacrifice for his sake (taking up our cross daily and following him). If this tonus relationship is watched carefully it will be seen that we bask in his love, and rest in him to such an extent that we, by setting out to be his disciples and serving and obeying him, win his confidence toward us, thus allowing him to take pleasure in our love.

The procedure of leaving out half of the dynamism of the Christian message has abstracted challenge from the Christian gospel, just as the ability to meet challenge would be taken out of a leg with only the extensor but no flexor muscle working. This process of making only half a dynamic system work not only removes ability to meet challenge; it also deforms the whole skeletal system and initiates muscle degeneration.

IDEALS IN COMMUNISTIC SOCIETIES

Need for Challenge Met

Over and against this picture of Western Christianity and society, Communist society has satiated its members with the "challenge" of idealistic socialism. The affluent society, on the one hand, has expended huge amounts of money and resources in its untiring effort to meet—and satiate—the purely material needs of its members. The Western world can only be lauded for this effort, even though it may have been misguided insofar as it is lopsided.

Communist society has, on the other hand, done very little until comparatively recently to satisfy the purely material needs of its members. But it has always done plenty to provide ideals which are propagated day and night, year in and year out, throughout Communistic and other countries. Their success is due to the fact that they are satisfying and meeting a basic need of humanity about which Western countries have done little. For all men need ideals of some sort. One hears that even newly engaged young couples in Moscow discuss the idealistic value of Marxist doctrine while dancing together.

Sacrifice for Ideals

Surely there is little doubt today that a percentage of idealistic Communists are so genuine in their idealistic belief that they will—and do—sacrifice their lives for the cause they live for. Part of this is because of the belief that the capitalist world is so degenerate and given to personal gain at the expense of the masses that the young Communist idealist feels obligated to dedicate his life—and death—to the destruction of the capitalist system by force. For his world is full of idealism, whereas the capitalist world is, in his eyes, decadent and devoid of real ideals.

In view of what we have said, then, about the necessity of challenge in human existence, is it any wonder that the Communist world has suffered far less from student revolts, juvenile delinquency, "Beatlemania," and drug epidemics than Western affluent society? One cannot attribute all the differences between the two societies in these respects to differing political powers. Even the false challenge of materialistic Marxist idealism functions for a time as does genuine challenge—until the disillusionment comes. Though it may be a long time in coming, as recent political history has shown.

THE SEARCH FOR CHALLENGE

Disproportionate Effort

In our society the effort put into the activity of meeting the material needs of the affluent society is disproportionately huge compared with the effort put into supplying its spiritual or psychical idealistic needs and individual challenges. The result of this disruption of balance between the two needs, the material and spiritual (or idealistic), leads to general malaise, particularly among the younger generation, where "deficiency" diseases often show up rapidly.

One does not get the impression that the leaders of the affluent society possess any real idea as to precisely what lies at the bottom of this general malaise of our younger generation. Although the police and the state have more power in the East than in the West, the difference in psychic health in the two areas would not seem to be due merely to differences in attitudes to police power. It would seem rather that in the East at present there is sufficient genuine, if misguided, challenge and idealism to prevent the lid from being blown off the seething pot containing the juvenile maelstrom—until even the East arrives at material satiation too!

Strike out in all directions. On the other hand, in the West the general malaise and lack of challenge, coupled with material satiation, has led to a process of striking out in every direction—against society, against authority and government, against teachers and even against parental control. It is exactly this process of hitting out and hitting back which helps us locate the neuralgic center of the basic disorder afflicting society. For, in the absence of legitimate challenge and hard work, the younger generation is caught up by synthetic challenge and synthetic work as well as a synthetic sense of achievement. The challenge and hard work involved in planning and conducting campaigns against police, society and parents, and of finding ways and means to lock up the president of the university in his own rooms or to smash the portraits of all the past presidents of the university (the symbols of present and of past authority), all this is their method of producing "muscular" or moral "tone." It is exciting and challenging to take up the cudgels against an authority (which so outnumbers the small band of crusaders) and to adopt new and better ideas and to translate them into radical action.

Some students and others have found artificial challenge in these violent types of activity. Others have resorted to a less muscular challenge, that of defying the law by taking hallucinatory drugs so as to be able to enter forbidden hallucinatory worlds of their own. This is also a challenge, even though a synthetic one. For one can never tell if the "trip" is going to be good or bad. Where there is no vision in real life, we find the younger generation generating artificial vision with all the infective abandon of youth—and the modern know-how of psychopharmacology.

THE CHRISTIAN MUST RESPOND

Bring out Christian Challenge

The urgent responsibility of those who propagate and attempt to live out the Christian message today is to take intelligent stock of the situation as it exists in the society in which they live. Where there has been little challenge it is imperative for us to bring out into full relief the real Christian challenge—to accept it and live it ourselves. For one side of the Christian challenge has been faithfully proclaimed in our Western society, the side emphasizing God's love toward man. But the other side—redeemed man wholeheartedly returning God's love, this compensating side of the Christian message, this corollary to the love of God—has been woefully understated by today's Christian society. The result has been insipid, a gospel lacking in challenge for young people who will always respond to a call such as Churchill's call to the British in 1940. He offered them only "blood, sweat and tears" in the service of their country against tyranny. They responded to a man.

The younger generation will respond to the challenge of "blood, sweat and tears" in the service of their Saviour when they see that he took on blood, sweat and tears for them. For he that would follow him *must* take up his cross *daily* and follow him. Instead of this true picture, the gospel too often offered today says that once a man or a woman gives his heart to God, all his problems will be resolved and life will be good fun ever afterward. If discipleship begins, then let us be sure that the trials of discipleship will begin too.

This side of the "muscle tone picture" is woefully missing today. So absent is it that the gospel has become almost irrelevant in wide circles in modern colleges and universities, no longer meeting the need for the challenge of physical or intellectual courage. Even the Peace Corps is better and more effective then contemporary Christianity in meeting this need for challenge, and thousands of young idealists join it every year and give to it their best efforts.

Affluence Could Be Used Effectively

Once the importance of this aspect of challenge is understood in our affluent society, our very affluence may become a little less dangerous than it is now. For it could be more effectively deployed in demonstrating to materially less fortunate individuals and societies how much the affluent Christian cares for them. The affluent Father God gave of his wealth, he gave his all—his very life—to redeem man. When the affluent Christian gives his reputation and his wealth in as unstinting a manner as did God the Father, then we shall experience the moving of his Spirit in this strife-torn world. For Christ, the affluent Son, became Christ, the "disadvantaged"! "Though he was rich, yet for our sakes he became poor."[5]

Here again, the question of "tonus" is vital, for as long as there is a hiatus between Christ's giving and the Christian's giving in respect to time, money, life or effort, our effectiveness in reaching others—the less fortunate both materially and spiritually—will be cramped and hindered. God's flexor side of the system has always been workable, but it can do nothing in this world without our extensor system working at full strength. Families and churches who have experienced the importance of these equilibria in their devotional and secular lives will find so much real challenge in the service of their King that the artificial drug and other challenges will pale before it like the moon when the sun comes up.

[1] Phil. 3:8.
[2] *Ibid.*
[3] Rom. 12:1-2; I John 2:15.
[4] Ps. 147:11, 149:4.
[5] II Cor. 8:9.

Glossary

Ablation. The removal of a part of the body, by excision or amputation.

Abreaction. The emotional discharge obtained after recall of psychic trauma during Freudian catharsis.

Acetylation. The introduction of an acetyl radical into an organic compound.

Addict. One who finds a habit (the taking of drugs) difficult to stop, and who may suffer withdrawal symptoms if his drug is stopped.

Adenochrome. A natural indole derivative which is related to serotonin.

Adept. One skilled or proficient (in the art of drug-taking).

Afferent. Conducting impulses *toward* a nerve center.

Agranulocytosis. An acute condition in which infected ulcers develop in the throat and other mucous membranes as well as in the skin.

Anaphrodisiac. That which lessens or destroys sexual desire.

Android. Resembling a man in form and structure.

Animism. The belief that all natural objects are endowed with indwelling souls.

Aphrodisiac. That which increases sexual desire.

Aqueous. Watery.

Astral. Super-terrestrial; relating to the stars.

Ataxia. Loss of the power of muscular coordination.

Botulism. A type of dangerous food poisoning.

Catharsis. Purging of the bowels.

Catecholamine. A natural stimulatory hormone of the body.

Choleric. Irascible; hot-tempered.

Comatose. In a state of coma or profound unconsciousness.

Conjunctivitis. Inflammation of the conjunctiva of the eye.

Contractility. The ability of a muscle to shorten or increase its tension.

Cumulative. Increasing by successive additions—as in dosing.

Deleterious. Hurtful; harmful; noxious.

Delirium tremens. Acute insanity due to alcoholic poisoning, marked by tremor, anxiety, mental confusion and hallucinations.

Dementia. General mental deterioration due to organic or emotional factors.

Dipsomania. A recurring compulsion to drink alcoholic beverages to excess.

Efferent. Conducting a nerve impulse *outward* from a nerve center.

Electroshock. The treatment of psychosis by the use of electric shock through the head.

Empirical. That which depends on experience or observation alone without regard to theory.

Engram. A trace on plant or animal protoplasm left by a stimulus, which, when regularly repeated, induces a persistent habit. Assuming that germ cells as well as nerve cells possess these engrams, acquired habits may thus be transmitted to descendants.

Enuresis. Involuntary reflex passage of urine, usually during sleep.

Ergine. An ergot derivative; lysergic acid amide.

Ergometer. An instrument for measuring muscular power.

Extra Sensory Perception (ESP). Perception not mediated by the five senses.

Ex nihilo. From, or out of nothing.

Flash Back. A psychedelic experience taking place without the immediate mediation of a drug.

Glia. A fibrous network supporting and enclosing nerves and cells of the brain and spinal cord.

Gastropod. Snail-like animal.

Glycogen. Animal starch.

Glycogenolysis. The conversion of glycogen into glucose.

Gorgonzola. An Italian milk cheese similar to Roquefort.

Gustatory. To do with taste.

Habitué. The subject of a habit.

Halflife. The time taken for a radioactive isotope or a drug within the body to lose half of its activity. This depends upon the rate at which the isotope is metabolized and excreted from the body.

Hegemony. Dominant influence or authority of a state or government.

Hyperesthesia. Abnormally increased sensitiveness (of the skin).

Hypochondria. Morbid concern about disease; exaggerated attention to bodily or mental symptoms.

Hypoglycemia. An abnormally small concentration of glucose in the circulating blood.

Hypothermia. Body temperature below 98.6°

In utero. Within the womb.

Kinesthetic. The sense perception of movement.

League for Spiritual Discovery. Movement initiated by Dr. Timothy Leary for the purpose of attaining religious experience through the use of hallucinogenic drugs.

Lesion. A wound or pathologic change in body tissue.

Leukemia. A malignant disease of the blood.

Lobotomy. Division of a nerve tract in a lobe of the cerebrum; a surgical treatment of emotional disease.

Macromolecular. Pertaining to molecules of large size.

Malaise. Feeling of general discomfort.

Malleability. Capability for being fashioned or molded.

Medicament. Medicine; remedy.

Micturation. Urination.

Miosis. Excessive contraction of the pupil of the eye.

Mucoid. Resembling mucus.

Myocarditis. Inflammation of the muscular walls of the heart.

Narcolepsy. Uncontrollable sleep.

Narcissism. Love of one's own body or personality.

Neonate. Newborn.

Neural. Relating to any part of the nervous system.

Obligate. Restricted to a single life condition.

Olfaction. The process or faculty of smelling.

Oneiritic, Oneiric. Pertaining to dreams.

Ostensible. Avowed; professed; apparent.

Oxidase. Enxyme that oxidizes chemical substances.

Oxytocic. Hastening childbirth.

Oxytocin. A hormone with uterine-contracting and milk-releasing action.

Paranoid, paranoia. A disorder of the mind characterized by delusions of persecution.

Pathological. Morbid; diseased; resulting from disease.

Peristalsis. A wavelike movement of alternate contraction and relaxation of intestines, or other tubelike structures, by which the contents are propelled onwards.

Phantasm. A specter, a mental image of a real object; an illusion.

Phantasmagoria. A shifting succession of things seen or imagined.

Placebo. An inert compound with the appearance of a medicine, given for suggestive effect.

Prima facie. First appearance or impression.

Proprioception. Reception of nerve impulses orienting the brain as to the position and state of the body.

Puerile. Childish.

Quasi-sensation. Apparent sensation.

Reverie. Day-dream; state of being lost in thought.

Serendipity. Adventitious chance discovery.

Serotonin. A substance occurring in various parts of the body and causing the constriction of blood vessels; its real function is unknown.

Sporadic. Occurring singly and spontaneously.

Substrate. A substance acted upon, as by an enzyme.

Synapse. The point of contact where a nerve impulse is transmitted from one neuron to another.

Synesthesia. A confusion of experiences, as when sound produces a sensation of color.

Systolic. Relating to contractions of the heart.

Tactile. Relating to the sense of touch.

Telesthesia. An impression received at a distance without the normal use of sense organs.

Thalamoreticular Relay. The nerve relay operating between the thalamus and the reticular areas.

Thymoleptic. An older term used to describe certain tranquilizing actions of drugs.

Vasoconstriction. Narrowing of the blood vessels.

Yoga. A mental discipline concentrating the attention on specific objects with a view to identification of the consciousness with the object.

Index

Bibliography

ABRAHAMSON, H. A. (ed.). *The Use of LSD in Psychotherapy and Alcoholism.* Indianapolis: Bobbs-Merrill, 1967.

ALSELSON, PHILIP. Editorial. *Science,* Vol. 159 (Mar. 15, 1968), No. 3820.

The Anatomy of Sleep. Nutley, N. J.: Roche Laboratories, 1966.

BERGSON, HENRI. *Matter and Memory.* New York: Macmillan, 1929.

BLUM, R. *et al. Utopiates: The Use and Users of LSD-25.* New York: Atherton, 1964.

BOGOCH, SAMUEL. *The Biochemistry of Memory.* New York: Oxford U., 1968.

BRADLEY, CHARLES, and BOWEN, MARGARET. "Amphetamine (Benzedrine) Therapy of Children's Behavior Disorders," *American Journal of Orthopsychiatry,* 11 (1941), 92-103.

BROAD, C. D. *Lectures on Psychical Research.* London: Routledge & Kegan Paul, 1962.

———. *Scientific Thought.* London: Routledge & Kegan Paul, 1952.

CARSTAIRS, G. M. "Daru and Bhang," *Quarterly Journal of Studies on Alcohol,* 15 (1954), 220-37.

COHEN, SIDNEY. *The Beyond Within—The LSD Story.* New York: Atheneum, 1964.

CONNELL, P. H. *Amphetamine Psychosis.* Maudesley Monograph No. 5. London: Oxford U., 1958.

CULBERTSON, JAMES T. *The Minds of Robots.* Urbana, Ill.: U. Illinois, 1963.

DEBOLD, R. C. and LEAF, RUSSELL C. (eds.). *LSD, Man and Society.* Middletown, Conn.: Wesleyan U., 1967.

DEMENT, WILLIAM C. and FISHER, CHARLES. *Further Experimental Studies on Dreaming.* Research Project Summaries, Public Health Service Publication No. 1208. Washington, D.C.:U.S. Government.

DEROPP, ROBERT S. *Drugs and the Mind.* New York: St. Martin's, 1957.

GADDUM, J. H. and HAMEED, K. A. "Drugs Which Antagonize 5-Hydroxy-Tryptamine," *British Journal of Pharmacology,* 9 (1954), 240.

EDDY, N.; HALBACH, H.; ISBELL, H.; and SEEVERS, M. H. *Drug Dependence: Its Significance and Characteristics,* Bulletin of World Health Organization, pp. 728-29.

FINK, M.; SIMEON, J.; HAGUE, W.; and ITIL, T. "Prolonged Adverse Reactions to LSD in Psychotic Subjects," *Arch. Gen. Psychiat.,* 15 (1966), 450.

GARDIBKAS, C. G. *Hashish and Crime.* 1950.

GHISELIN, BREWSTER (ed.), *The Creative Process.* Berkeley, Calif.: U. California, 1952.

GOODMAN, LOUIS S. and GILMAN, AFRED (eds.). *The Pharmacological Basis of Therapeutics.* New York: Macmillan, 1965.

HANSEL, C. E. M. *ESP, A Scientific Evaluation.* New York: Scribner, 1966.

HATT, HAROLD E. *Cybernetics and the Image of Man.* Nashville: Abingdon, 1968.

HENTOFF, NAT. *A Doctor Among the Addicts.* Chicago: Rand McNally, 1968.

HERXHEIMER, ANDREW (ed.). *Drugs and Sensory Functions.* London: Churchill, 1968.

HESSE, ERICH. *Narcotics and Drug Addiction.* New York: Philosophical Library, 1946.

HOFFER, ABRAM and OSMOND, HUMPHRY. "A Card Sorting Test Helpful in Making Psychiatric Diagnosis," *Journal of Neuropsychiatry, 2 (1961), 306.*

———. *The Hallucinogens.* New York: Academic, 1967.

———. "Malvaria: A New Psychiatric Disease," *Acta Psychiatria Scandinavica,* 39 (1963), 335.

———. "Some Problems of Stochastic Psychiatry," *Journal of Neuropsychiatry,* 5 (1964), 97.

HUTTEN, KURT. *Iron Curtain Christians.* Minneapolis: Augsburg, 1967.

HUXLEY, ALDOUS. *Doors of Perception.* New York: Harper, 1954.

HYDE, MARGARET O. (ed.). *Mind Drugs.* New York: McGraw-Hill, 1968.

JARMAN, R. C. "The Most Astounding Experience of My Life," sermon, *Chapel Bells.* South Gate, Calif., 1961.

JEANS, SIR JAMES. *The Mysterious Universe.* New York: MacMillan, 1932.

JOACHIMOGLU, G. "Natural and Smoked Hashish," CIBA Foundation Study Group No. 21, *Hashish, Its Chemistry and Pharmacology.* 1965.

KAST, E. C. "The Analgesic Action of LSD Compared with Dihydromorphinone and Meperidine," *Bulletin of Drug Addiction and Narcotics,* 27 (1963), 3517.

———. "A Study of LSD as an Analgesic Agent," *Anaesthesia and Analgesia,* 43 (1964), 285.

———. "LSD and the Dying Patient," *Chicago Medical School Quarterly,* Vol. 26 (1966), No. 2, p. 80.

KAST, E. C. and COLLINS, V. J. "Study of Lysergic Acid Diethylamide as an Analgesic Agent," *Journal of Intern. Anesthet. Res. Soc.,* 43 (1964), 285.

LAURIE, PETER. *Drugs*. Baltimore: Penguin, 1967.

LEAKE, CHAUNCEY D. *The Amphetamines*. Springfield, Ill.: Thomas, 1958.

LEARY, TIMOTHY. *The Politics of Ecstasy*. New York: Putnam, 1968.

LEWIS, C. S. *The Screwtape Letters and Screwtape Proposes a Toast*. London: Geoffrey Bles, 1961.

LOURIA, DONALD B. and SOKOLOW, M. *Nightmare Drugs*. New York: Simon & Schuster, 1966.

MAURER, DAVID W. and VOGEL, VICTOR H. *Narcotics and Narcotic Addiction*. 2d ed.; Springfield, Ill.: Thomas, 1962.

MILLER, DONALD E. *Narcotic Drug and Marijuana Controls*, National Association of Student Personnel Administrators, Drug Education Project, 1966-67.

O'DONNELL, JOHN A.; BALL, JOHN C.; and ISBELL, HARRIS (eds.). *Narcotic Addiction*. New York: Harper & Row, 1966.

OSMOND, H. "A Review of the Effects of Psychotomimetic Agents," *Ann. N.Y. Acad. Sc.*, 66 (1957), 429.

PAHNKE, WALTER N. and RICHARDS, W. A. "Implication of LSD and Experimental Mysticism," *Journal of Religious Health*, 513 (1966), 175.

Report of the Indian Hemp Drug Commission. Government of India, 1893-94.

SOLOMON, DAVID. *The Marijuana Papers*. Indianapolis: Bobbs-Merrill, 1966.

STUART, K. L. "Ganja/Cannabis sativa L." Review. *W. L. Medical Journal*, 12 (1963), 159.

TART, CHARLES E. (ed.). *Altered States of Consciousness*. New York: John Wiley & Sons, Inc., 1969.

United Nations Document E/CN 7/1 268 (May 14, 1965).

WELCH, J. H. "Marine Invertebrate Preparations Useful in the Bioassay of Acetylcholine and 5-Hydroxytryptamine," *Nature*, 173 (1954), 955.

WEST, L. J. and PIERCE, C. M. "LSD, Its Effects on a Male Asiatic Elephant," *Science*, 138 (1962), 1100.

WILDER SMITH, A. E. *Man's Origin, Man's Destiny*. Wheaton, Ill.: Shaw, 1968.

WILSON, C. W. M. (ed.). *Adolescent Drug Dependence*. London: Pergamon, 1968.

WITT, P. N. *The Effect of Substances on the Construction of Webs by Spiders as a Biological Test*. Berlin: Springer, 1956.

WOLMAN, BENJAMIN B. *The Unconscious Mind*. Englewood Cliffs, N.J.: Prentice-Hall, 1968.